TEST YOUR WORD POWER

By the same author

PROGRESSIVE BRAIN-TEASING QUIZZES
THE ALL-BRITISH QUIZ BOOK

TEST
YOUR
WORD POWER

by
JOHN G. BARTON

PAPERFRONTS

ELLIOT RIGHT WAY BOOKS,
KINGSWOOD, SURREY, U.K.

Printed and bound in Great Britain by
Cox & Wyman Ltd, Reading

To
Anne – Louise
and
Jeremy

Contents

Introduction

There are about 500,000 words in the English language – plus 300,000 technical terms. The number of words used in ordinary written English however is a mere 10,000. The average person uses in speech only 2,000 – 3,000 words, a highly-educated person about 5,000.

But more important than the number of words you use is the number of words that you know the precise meaning of. How often do you read a word in a book or newspaper and guess its meaning without bothering to look it up in a dictionary? How often do you write or speak a word which you know is not quite the right one because you cannot think of a better one?

The aim of this book is to test your knowledge of many of the words commonly used in written and spoken English. As an added interest, and to enlarge your vocabulary, there are some questions on the more uncommon words that are met with only occasionally.

Each set of answers follows immediately after the questions, but sometimes there are three consecutive question pages with the answers all on one page, and sometimes one question page with the answers on three consecutive pages.

The meanings of most of the words used in this book are taken from the *Shorter Oxford English Dictionary*, 3rd. edition 1955, by kind permission of The Clarendon Press, Oxford.

J.G.B.

Acknowledgement

The Author and Publisher wish to acknowledge with gratitude some use made of the *Shorter Oxford English Dictionary*, third edition, 1955, by kind permission of The Clarendon Press, Oxford.

Animal Words

Canine is the adjective relating to dogs, from *canis*, the Latin word for dog. To which animals do these words refer?

1. Aquiline	9. Asinine	17. Saurian
2. Bovine	10. Vulpine	18. Piscine
3. Ursine	11. Lupine	19. Avian
4. Feline	12. Soricine	20. Simian
5. Porcine	13. Cervine	21. Murine
6. Leonine	14. Leporine	22. Vespine
7. Equine	15. Sciurine	23. Hircine
8. Ovine	16. Elephantine	24. Hirudinal

*   *   *

A group or collection of cattle is known as a *herd*. What is the word for a group of these animals?

1. Squirrels	9. Ravens	17. Racehorses
2. Lions	10. Frogs	18. Kangaroos
3. Foxes	11. Starlings	19. Grouse
4. Nightingales	12. Rooks	20. Chickens
5. Bees	13. Hounds	21. Geese
6. Crows	14. Larks	(on water)
7. Elephants	15. Gulls	22. Leopards
8. Eagles	16. Storks	23. Rhinoceroses
		24. Porpoises

Animal Words

1. Eagles	9. Asses	17. Lizards
2. Oxen	10. Foxes	18. Fish
3. Bears	11. Wolves	19. Birds
4. Cats	12. Shrew-mice	20. Apes
5. Swine	13. Deer	21. Mice
6. Lions	14. Hares	22. Wasps
7. Horses	15. Squirrels	23. Goats
8. Sheep	16. Elephants	24. Leeches

*   *   *

1. Dray	9. Unkindness	17. String
2. Pride, flock or troop	10. Army	18. Troop
	11. Chattering	19. Covey or pack
3. Skulk or earth	12. Clamour	20. Brood
4. Watch	13. Pack	21. Gaggle
5. Swarm	14. Exaltation	22. Leap
6. Murder	15. Colony	23. Crash
7. Herd	16. Mustering	24. School
8. Convocation		

What Does This Word Mean? No. 1

Give the meanings of these words.

1. Abyss	25. Bacciform	49. Cabal
2. Acme	26. Bakelite	50. Cacophony
3. Acrimony	27. Barbican	51. Cajole
4. Aerobe	28. Baroque	52. Callisthenics
5. Affray	29. Beatification	53. Candour
6. Akimbo	30. Bedraggled	54. Casement
7. Alfresco	31. Bellicose	55. Censer
8. Alidade	32. Berserk	56. Cephalic
9. Allergy	33. Bibliophile	57. Chagrin
10. Amalgam	34. Bicentennial	58. Charlatan
11. Amnesia	35. Biograph	59. Chide
12. Amorphous	36. Bipurtite	60. Circumlocution
13. Anathema	37. Blatant	61. Clandestine
14. Anodyne	38. Blather	62. Clarity
15. Antediluvian	39. Bludgeon	63. Clientele
16. Aperient	40. Bombast	64. Cognizant
17. Aplomb	41. Brachylogy	65. Collimate
18. Apophthegm	42. Bravado	66. Conflagration
19. Arenaceous	43. Breviary	67. Criterion
20. Astrolabe	44. Bric-a-brac	68. Crucible
21. Auger	45. Browbeat	69. Cryptic
22. Augury	46. Brusque	70. Cupreous
23. Avuncular	47. Bullace	71. Curtilage
24. Axial	48. Burgeon	72. Cygnet

What Does This Word Mean? No. 1

1. a bottomless chasm, deep gorge, bowels of the eathr
2. the highest point or pitch, the culmination or perfection
3. bitterness of temper or manner
4. a microbe living on free oxygen from the air
5. a breach of the peace, caused by fighting in a public place
6. hand on hip and elbow turned outward
7. in the open air
8. a surveying instrument, or part of one, which measures vertical angles
9. sensitiveness to certain foods, insect bites, etc.
10. mixture of metal with mercury, mixture of any two substances
11. loss of memory
12. shapeless, formless
13. an accursed thing, curse of the Church, an imprecation
14. medicine or drug which alleviates pain, anything soothing
15. relating or referring to the period before the Flood
16. laxative
17. confidence, self-possession, perpendicularity
18. a terse, pointed saying, a pithy maxim
19. sandy, sand-like (referring to soils)
20. an instrument formerly used for taking altitudes
21. a tool for boring holes in wood or in the earth
22. an omen, portent, presentiment
23. of or like an uncle
24. round an axis, forming an axis

What Does This Word Mean?
No. 1

25. berry-shaped
26. a synthetic resin or plastic
27. an outer defence to a city or castle
28. grotesque, odd (especially of a style of architecture)
29. the action of making, or being made, blessed
30. hanging or trailing limply wet
31. inclined to war, warlike
32. a state of frenzied fury
33. a lover of books
34. occurring every two hundred years, lasting two hundred years
35. an early form of cinematograph
36. divided into two parts, drawn up in two parts
37. noisy, clamorous, offensively loud
38. loquacious nonsense
39. a short stick or club used as a weapon, to strike with one
40. inflated, turgid or empty language
41. condensed expression, over-conciseness of speech
42. boastful behaviour or show of courage
43. a brief statement, the book containing the 'Divine Office'
44. old curiosities, antiquarian odds-and-ends
45. to bully, bear down with words or looks
46. blunt, offhand (of manner or speech)
47. wild plum tree, wild plum
48. to put forth buds, to sprout, a young bud

What Does This Word Mean?
No. 1

49. a private intrigue, secret meeting, clique
50. an ill sound or discord
51. to persuade by flattery, specious promises, deceit etc.
52. exercises (esp. for girls) for developing the figure
53. frankness, ingenuousness
54. type of window-frame
55. a vessel in which incense is burnt
56. of or relating to the head
57. mortification arising from disappointment or failure
58. an impostor, quack, pretender to knowledge
59. to scold, rebuke
60. the use of many words instead of few, a roundabout expression
61. secret, concealed, underhand, surreptitious
62. clearness
63. a body of clients, supporters or customers, a following
64. having knowledge of, being aware of
65. to adjust line of sight (of telescopes), make parallel
66. a large, destructive fire
67. a principle or standard by which something is judged
68. a vessel made to endure great heat, a severe trial
69. secret, occult, mystical
70. of or containing copper, copper-coloured
71. an area attached to a house, forming one enclosure with it
72. a young swan

The Right Word

Select the word in each group of four which is nearest in meaning to the given word.

1. Acumen (courage, intelligence, discernment, veracity)
2. Alacrity (bitterness, promptitude, lateness, fortitude)
3. Ameliorate (lessen, teach, polish, improve)
4. Antipathy (pity, aversion, sympathy, contempt)
5. Astringent (severe, acid, biting, soothing)
6. Bane (upset, cause, curse, flower)
7. Blithe (lonely, contented, gay, active)
8. Cant (slang, wordiness, falsehood, insincerity)
9. Caprice (anger, whim, friction, chance)
10. Cavil (find fault, show off, threaten, embezzle)
11. Compendium (suitcase, holdall, summary, dictionary)
12. Concoct (make up, lie, slander, fulfil)
13. Consummate (complete, add, subtract, defer)
14. Convulse (miss out, pass over, throw, agitate)
15. Corrugated (rusty, grooved, corroded, bent)
16. Coy (backward, naïve, bashful, imperfect)
17. Diatribe (lecture, sect, reason, invective)
18. Diffuse (dispersed, distorted, obscure, clear)
19. Élan (precision, dash, smoothness, virility)
20. Equivocal (equal, horse-like, ambiguous, ambitious)
21. Euphory (well-being, praise, esteem, gaiety)
22. Flamboyant (brash, active, overbearing, florid)
23. Grisly (bear-like, fatty, ghastly, whining)
24. Heretical (spiral, unorthodox, sealed, old)

Answers on page 20

The Right Word

25. Hypothesis (assumption, reverse, opposite, zenith)
26. Lacerate (upset, divide, tear, inconvenience)
27. Languor (suavity, ease, lassitude, rest)
28. Lank (lean, damp, uneven, thick)
29. Libidinous (extravagant, thrifty, illiterate, lustful)
30. Lineament (ointment, feature, medicine, pedigree)
31. Malevolent (evil, irate, mistaken, ill-mannered)
32. Manifest (grievous, loud, evident, handy)
33. Maudlin (pitiful, sentimental, ringing, melancholy)
34. Mensuration (judgement, measurement, incivility, pain)
35. Misanthrope (miser, melancholic, witch, man-hater)
36. Miscreant (wanderer, spendthrift, minister, villain)
37. Modicum (little, mean, middling, medium)
38. Mullion (mineral, servant, window-bar, treasure)
39. Pallid (distressed, pale, poor, superficial)
40. Panacea (remedy, plant, blight, disease)
41. Pathetic (evoking pity, incompetent, poor, medicinal)
42. Pedagogy (act of walking, chiropody, logic, instruction)
43. Peregrination (bird-watching, divination, journey, cookery)
44. Pertinent (rude, relevant, precise, tidy)
45. Plebeian (banal, flighty, socialistic, lower-class)
46. Plenary (absolute, penal, plentiful, mean)
47. Plethora (swelling, dogma, excess, profit)
48. Polemic (poisonous, libellous, devious, controversial)

Answers on page 20

The Right Word

49. Pretext (excuse, design, prologue, skill)
50. Prim (neat, prudish, naïve, upright)
51. Raillery (slander, ridicule, illegal act, oration)
52. Ratify (excuse, reason, confirm, regard)
53. Regale (entertain, conflict, pass over, lose)
54. Riparian (wild, carnivorous, pertaining to river-banks, primitive)
55. Rue (pity, look over, die, regret)
56. Sanctimony (gratefulness, assumed piety, greed, refuge)
57. Sarcastic (cutting, uneven, bad-tempered, evil)
58. Sidereal (crippled, sedentary, everlasting, relating to the stars)
59. Sinecure (priest, office without duties, type of chair, medicine)
60. Sophisticated (clever, bright, logical, worldy-wise)
61. Spasmodic (intermittent, illegible, diseased, shoddy)
62. Staid (upright, sedate, retired, unbroken)
63. Stertorous (ponderous, questionable, loud, snoring heavily)
64. Stigma (reputation, promise, mark of disgrace, part of a flower)
65. Stultify (render useless, stifle, stunt, speak out)
66. Succinct (concise, sarcastic, sudden, early)
67. Succulent (growing, juicy, young, empty)
68. Supercilious (inconsequent, intangible, witty, haughtily superior)
69. Tarnish (paint, improve, stain, destroy)
70. Tenebrous (slender, gloomy, tenacious, genuine)
71. Termagant (lizard, sea-bird, legal officer, quarrelsome woman)
72. Turpitude (depravity, laziness, dirtiness, greed)

The Right Word

1. discernment
2. promptitude
3. improve
4. aversion
5. severe
6. curse
7. gay
8. insincerity
9. whim
10. find fault
11. summary
12. make up
13. complete
14. agitate
15. grooved
16. bashful
17. invective
18. dispersed
19. dash
20. ambiguous
21. well-being
22. florid
23. ghastly
24. unorthodox
25. assumption
26. tear
27. lassitude
28. lean
29. lustful
30. feature
31. evil
32. evident
33. sentimental
34. measurement
35. man-hater
36. villain
37. little
38. window-bar
39. pale
40. remedy
41. evoking pity
42. instruction
43. journey
44. relevant
45. lower-class
46. absolute
47. excess
48. controversial
49. excuse
50. prudish
51. ridicule
52. confirm
53. entertain
54. pertaining to river-banks
55. regret
56. assumed piety
57. cutting
58. relating to the stars
59. office without duties
60. worldly-wise
61. intermittent
62. sedate
63. snoring heavily
64. mark of disgrace
65. render useless
66. concise
67. juicy
68. haughtily superior
69. stain
70. gloomy
71. quarrelsome woman
72. depravity

Odd Man Out

In each of the following groups all the words except one have approximately the same meaning. Which is the odd one out in each group and what is its meaning?

1. Languor, quiescence, lassitude, lethargy
2. Phlegmatic, stolid, stupid, sluggish
3. Dolorous, dismal, mournful, unmusical
4. Obstinate, assiduous, diligent, persevering
5. Astringent, ruthless, severe, austere
6. Incongruous, inconvenient, incompatible, discrepant
7. Punctilious, scrupulous, consistent, conscientious
8. Protuberant, distended, tumid, demented
9. Virulent, malignant, jejune, toxic
10. Oppressive, ravenous, rapacious, voracious
11. Debonair, modish, urbane, suave
12. Mendacious, fickle, untruthful, fictitious
13. Germane, apposite, pertinent, conducive
14. Mephitic, noxious, salacious, insalubrious
15. Precocious, naughty, premature, advanced
16. Perspicuous, discriminating, lucid, explicit
17. Desultory, refractory, contumacious, recalcitrant
18. Cacophonous, discordant, indecorous, dissonant
19. Specious, convincing, plausible, ostensible
20. Insouciant, egregious, prodigious, monstrous
21. Imply, insinuate, correspond, hint
22. Incipient, inchoate, incoherent, rudimentary
23. Concurrent, co-existent, concomitant, contingent
24. Exculpate, sequestrate, exonerate, acquit

Odd Man Out

1. Quiescence – quietness, immobility
2. Stupid – slow-witted, dull, obtuse
3. Unmusical – not musical, inharmonious
4. Obstinate – stubborn, inflexible
5. Ruthless – without pity or compassion
6. Inconvenient – awkward, troublesome, unsuitable
7. Consistent – compatible, not contradictory
8. Demented – crazed, insane
9. Jejune – unsatisfying, dull, insipid
10. Oppressive – overpowering, overwhelming
11. Modish – Fashionable
12. Fickle – inconstant, changeable
13. Conducive – leading to or contributing to
14. Salacious – lustful, lecherous
15. Naughty – disobedient, ill-behaved
16. Discriminating – making a distinction, differentiating
17. Desultory – unmethodical, skipping about, random
18. Indecorous – in bad taste, improper
19. Convincing – persuasive, carrying conviction
20. Insouciant – careless, indifferent, unconcerned
21. Correspond – be in harmony, similar to, communicate
22. Incoherent – not connected, disjointed
23. Contingent – incidental to, conditional, accidental
24. Sequestrate – appropriate, confiscate, seize possession of

Complete the Word — A

Complete the following words from the given meanings.

1. A . . c . . a counting-frame with balls on wires
2. A . t . . c . t . to dispute or wrangle
3. A . r . g . t . to repeal, cancel
4. Ap . . l . . n the point farthest from the sun in a planet's orbit
5. A . g . . t . . . like silver
6. A . m . n . . h to warn, remind, inform or reprove
7. A . . m . . v . . t to criticize or censure
8. A . s . . . h a liqueur made from wormwood
9. A . h . . m . . . c free from colour
10. As . . v . . . t . to solemnly declare, to assert
11. A . . m . . t stubborn, resolute
12. A . t . f . . . a product of human work or art
13. A . . r . b . t . to assign or ascribe to
14. A . . m . r . t . to outline, indicate, foreshadow
15. A . q . . . s . . to agree or accept
16. A . t . . . c . . c a type of coal
17. An . . . r . . . a hermit
18. A . r . . . y to waste away
19. A . . . m . n animal substance, found in the white of eggs
20. A . t . . m . . . . m a defect in the focus of the eye
21. A . r . f . . . u . yielding gold
22. Am . . u . n . . s one who writes from dictation
23. A . . th . . s . . canonization, deification
24. A . l . t . . . t . . n words in close proximity with same first letter

Answers on page 26

Complete the Word — B

Complete the following words from the given meanings.

1. B . . v . . .   shortness, conciseness
2. B . . nd . . . m . . t   a flattering or coaxing speech or action
3. B . st . . d . .   a spectator
4. B . . r . . . d .   a West Indian fish
5. B . . . . t   a bunch of flowers
6. B . v . . ag .   a drink
7. B . . c . . l .   a type of vegetable
8. B . . l . . . u .   an imitation, caricature, parody
9. B . . z . .   a shield, coat of arms
10. B . t . m . .   mineral pitch, asphalt
11. B . c . . . . t   a card game
12. B . . b . . .   whale fat
13. B . . w . r .   a rampart or defence
14. B . g . . . l . .   a short piece of music, also a game
15. B . . r . . . . s . .   the middle-class
16. B . f . . c . . .   to branch into two, to fork
17. B . . f . . n   a comic or jester
18. Br . . . . . m   a type of carriage
19. B . z . . r .   grotesque, fantastic
20. B . q . . . t .   to leave by will
21. B . m . . . z . .   to mystify or cheat somebody
22. B . . g . . . . n .   a two-masted vessel
23. Br . . d . . .   to wave about, flourish
24. B . . st . . . . s   rough, noisy

Answers on page 26

Complete the Word — C

Complete the following words from the given meanings.

1. C . . l . p . . n .   a transparent wrapping material
2. C . . y . . r .   an old Scottish sword
3. C . . v . . . .   a small naval vessel
4. C . n . c . .   sneering, derisive
5. C . t . s . . . p . .   a disaster, calamity
6. C . t . . . l   a fortress or castle
7. C . . s . . c . . . s   class of animals with hard shells
8. C . l . . t .   to compare in detail
9. C . t . c . . . s   underground cemeteries or chambers
10. C . b . . . t   a kind of entertainment
11. C . p . . c . . . s   subject to whim, inconstant
12. C . n . . t . n . t .   to link together
13. C . . l . . . c   angry, irascible
14. C . h . . .   to stick together
15. C . . h . . t   a type of whale
16. C . . t l   tending to fly off from the centre
17. C . c . . . n . t .   to laugh loudly
18. C . . t . m . . i . . .   disobedient, insubordinate
19. C . . ff . . . . r   type of low cupboard with a top
20. C . . g . l . . .   to solidify or clot
21. C . r . . r . . d . m   a polishing-stone
22. C . m . . . b . . d   a waist-sash
23. Cr . . . l . . . . d   furnished with battlements
24. C . . k . . .   the husband of an unfaithful wife

Complete the Word

A	B	C
1. Abacus	1. Brevity	1. Cellophane
2. Altercate	2. Blandishment	2. Claymore
3. Abrogate	3. Bystander	3. Corvette
4. Aphelion	4. Barracuda	4. Cynical
5. Argentine	5. Bouquet	5. Catastrophe
6. Admonish	6. Beverage	6. Citadel
7. Animadvert	7. Broccoli	7. Crustaceans
8. Absinth	8. Burlesque	8. Collate
9. Achromatic	9. Blazon	9. Catacombs
10. Asseverate	10. Bitumen	10. Cabaret
11. Adamant	11. Baccarat	11. Capricious
12. Artefact	12. Blubber	12. Concatenate
13. Attribute	13. Bulwark	13. Choleric
14. Adumbrate	14. Bagatelle	14. Cohere
15. Acquiesce	15. Bourgeoisie	15. Cachalot
16. Anthracite	16. Bifurcate	16. Centrifugal
17. Anchorite	17. Buffoon	17. Cachinnate
18. Atrophy	18. Brougham	18. Contumacious
19. Albumen	19. Bizarre	19. Chiffonier
20. Astigmatism	20. Bequeath	20. Coagulate
21. Auriferous	21. Bamboozle	21. Carborundum
22. Amanuensis	22. Brigantine	22. Cummerbund
23. Apotheosis	23. Brandish	23. Crenellated
24. Alliteration	24. Boisterous	24. Cuckold

Why is it Called That?

The derivation and origin of words is a fascinating study or science known as *etymology*. The following words have exceptionally interesting derivations – do you know what they are?

1. Steeplechase	25. America
2. Cardigan	26. Galvanize
3. Drawing-room	27. January
4. Maverick	28. February
5. Matinée	29. March
6. Tarmacadam	30. April
7. Canter	31. May
8. Gerrymander	32. June
9. Ambulance	33. July
10. Boycott	34. August
11. Corduroy	35. September
12. Mesmerize	36. Guillotine
13. Foolscap	37. Mausoleum
14. Sadism	38. Hansom
15. Funny-bone	39. Omnibus
16. Sandwich	40. Macintosh
17. Honeymoon	41. Dahlia
18. Wellington	42. Sunday
19. Santa Claus	43. Monday
20. Shrapnel	44. Tuesday
21. Tenterhooks	45. Wednesday
22. Silhouette	46. Thursday
23. Derrick	47. Friday
24. Panic	48. Saturday

Why is it Called That?

1. Originally this name was given to a horse-race across country with a church steeple in view as the winning-post.
2. A woollen waistcoat named after the 7th Earl (of Crimean fame).
3. Formerly *withdrawing-room*, a room to which the ladies withdrew after dinner.
4. Named after a Texan rancher whose unbranded cattle became known as 'mavericks'; now applied to any roving person.
5. From the French *matin* = morning, formerly applied to a morning theatrical or musical performance.
6. A type of road-surfacing, after its inventor John Macadam.
7. From 'Canterbury gallop', which was the usual pace of the medieval pilgrims travelling to Canterbury.
8. An unfair electoral system, named after Governor Gerry of Massachusetts who first adopted it.
9. Derived from the French *hôpital ambulant* – 'walking hospital' i.e. the first-aid litters of the early 19th-century wars.
10. After Captain Boycott, Lord Erne's estate agent in Ireland, who was persecuted by the Irish Land League.
11. From the French *corde du roi*, a material formerly made from silk and used only by the Kings.
12. After Franz Mesmer, Austrian physician, who first propounded the theory of 'animal magnetism'.
13. A watermark of a fool's cap formerly used in printing paper.
14. A perversion named after the infamous Count de Sade.
15. Said to be a pun on *humerus*, which is the real name of the bone in the elbow which produces pain when struck.

Why is it Called That?

16. Named after the 4th Earl of Sandwich, who thought of the idea, it is said, to keep him going at the gaming-table!
17. It was once the practice for newly-weds to drink honey-wine for the first month (or moon) after marriage.
18. Named after the first Duke, perhaps as a compliment.
19. From the Dutch *Sante Klaas* – Saint Nicholas.
20. After General Henry Shrapnel, who invented it.
21. A tenter is a framework with hooks for stretching woven cloth, so to be on tenterhooks is to be under great strain or tension.
22. Named after the 18th-century French finance minister, whose hobby was cutting out paper portraits.
23. From a hangman of that name; subsequently applied to a gallows, then to a crane or hoist.
24. From the Greek *panikos* – of or attributable to the god Pan.
25. Named after Amerigo Vespucci (1452–1512), Italian explorer, who sailed along the South American coasts but certainly did not discover them.
26. From Galvani, who first described the process of galvanism.
27. From the Latin *Januarius* – the month of Janus, a Roman god regarded as presiding over the entrance to the year.
28. From the Latin *februarius*, a festival of purification held in that month.
29. The Roman month *Martius*, from the god Mars.
30. Derivation uncertain, but perhaps from the Latin *aperire* to open, i.e. the season when flowers start to open.

Why is it Called That?

31. Latin *maius*, perhaps derived from the goddess Maia, or perhaps from the root *mag* – to grow (the growing season).
32. From the Latin *Junius*, probably from the goddess Juno.
33. Named after Julius Caesar.
34. Named after Augustus Caesar.
35. From the Latin *septem* – seven, it being the seventh month in the old Roman calendar. (As October, November, December were the eighth, ninth and tenth months.)
36. Named after M. Guillotin, who in 1789 advocated the revival of this old instrument of decapitation.
37. After King Mausolus of Caria and his splendid tomb.
38. After Joseph Hansom who in 1834 invented a safety cab.
39. A Latin word meaning 'for all'; now a vehicle 'for all'.
40. After its inventor, Charles Macintosh.
41. Named in honour of the Swedish botanist Dahl.
42. The 'day of the sun'.
43. The 'day of the moon'.
44. From Tiw, a Teutonic god.
45. From the god Woden.
46. From the god Thunor.
47. From the Teutonic goddess Frig.
48. The day of the planet Saturn.

Can It Be True?

Some words are so odd-looking that one can hardly believe they are real words. Can you pick out the 24 real words from this list and give their meaning? Give yourself one mark for each one identified and two extra marks if you also know its meaning.

1. Alten	25. Snig	49. Woof
2. Ginglyform	26. Enery	50. Weemster
3. Eventate	27. Tiesome	51. Grunge
4. Digo	28. Bufflehead	52. Whelving
5. Plentitude	29. Plurry	53. Thistly
6. Understrapper	30. Splurge	54. Ha-ha
7. Brime	31. Sidget	55. Drocket
8. Earthling	32. Priverous	56. Superglies
9. Chapet	33. Pockety	57. Drabble
10. Dicropter	34. Midan	58. Stinwall
11. Scapple	35. Epopt	59. Prurn
12. Ravenish	36. Bumbelo	60. Samekin
13. Niddling	37. Sparilate	61. Quackle
14. Absquatulate	38. Cliable	62. Purgeon
15. Middock	39. Odoom	63. Fenks
16. Cosmoloquy	40. Snurd	64. Neegle
17. Melodion	41. Phluted	65. Inclaim
18. Residant	42. Alestered	66. Absernation
19. Dumbrage	43. Brandage	67. Abfer
20. Gorble	44. Rejectamenta	68. Eoan
21. Niddering	45. Smollish	69. Plimwheel
22. Zinky	46. Interferometer	70. Cogelly
23. Fusture	47. Emolve	71. Flart
24. Habitament	48. Snit	72. Subnumate

31

Can It Be True?

These are the real words and their meanings.

2. Ginglyform – hinge-shaped.
6. Understrapper – a subordinate, an underling.
8. Earthling – an inhabitant of the earth.
11. Scapple – to reduce the faces of a stone block to a plane surface.
14. Absquatulate – to leave hurriedly, to abscond.
17. Melodion – an obsolete wind instrument, a type of accordion.
21. Niddering – a coward; base or cowardly.
22. Zinky – relating to or containing zinc.
25. Snig – a young or small eel.
28. Bufflehead – a fool, a blockhead.
30. Splurge – ostentatious display, heavy splash.
33. Pockety – said of a mine having pockets of ore.
35. Epopt – a beholder.
36. Bumbelo – a glass vessel for subliming camphor.
39. Odoom – a West African timber tree.
44. Rejectamenta – useless or worthless things, refuse.
46. Interferometer – instrument for measuring lengths by rays of light.
49. Woof – woven fabric or thread.
53. Thistly – like a thistle, full of thistles.
54. Ha-ha – a sunken fence or boundary.
57. Drabble – to become wet and dirty, to fish with rod and line.
61. Quackle – to quack like a duck.
63. Fenks – the parts of the whale blubber which contain oil.
68. Eoan – pertaining to the dawn, eastern.

What Does This Word Mean?
No. 2

Give the meanings of these words.

1. Dais	25. Ebullient	49. Facile
2. Dawdle	26. Echelon	50. Factitious
3. Debilitate	27. Eclogue	51. Faience
4. Debonair	28. Educe	52. Fallible
5. Decrepit	29. Effete	53. Fastidious
6. Deflagrate	30. Effulgent	54. Fecund
7. Demoniac	31. Egregious	55. Ferrule
8. Denizen	32. Electrode	56. Fervour
9. Depilate	33. Elision	57. Figurine
10. Dermatology	34. Emanate	58. Fissile
11. Diaphanous	35. Emolument	59. Flagrant
12. Didactic	36. Encomium	60. Flatulent
13. Dilatory	37. Ennui	61. Flippant
14. Discrepant	38. Ephemeral	62. Flocculent
15. Disquisition	39. Epigram	63. Foliage
16. Dodecagon	40. Epitaph	64. Formulate
17. Dolorous	41. Epithet	65. Fortuitous
18. Dragoman	42. Epitome	66. Fractious
19. Drollery	43. Erudite	67. Fructify
20. Drowsy	44. Estimable	68. Fugacious
21. Dryad	45. Eulogize	69. Fumigate
22. Dudgeon	46. Evaluate	70. Funereal
23. Dulcet	47. Evoke	71. Furbish
24. Dyne	48. Exegesis	72. Furore

What Does This Word Mean? No. 2

1. a raised platform
2. to idle, loiter, waste time
3. to enfeeble, make weak
4. genial, pleasant, affable
5. worn out with age, old and feeble
6. to cause to burn away rapidly, to burst into flame and burn rapidly
7. devilish, like a demon, possessed by an evil spirit
8. an inhabitant or occupant, a foreigner admitted to residence
9. to remove the hair from
10. the science of the skin and its diseases
11. permitting light to pass through, transparent
12. having the manner of a teacher, instructive
13. tending to cause or designed to cause delay, given to delay
14. dissimilar, discordant, inconsistent
15. a lengthy treatise or discourse on a subject
16. a plane figure of twelve sides and angles
17. dismal, doleful, distressing
18. an interpreter or guide in the Middle East
19. quaint humour, jesting
20. sleepy, sluggish, soporific
21. a tree- or wood-nymph
22. a feeling of anger, resentment or offence
23. sweet to the ear, pleasing, soothing
24. a unit of force

What Does This Word Mean?
No. 2

25. boiling, exuberant, bubbling over
26. formation of troops etc., in which divisions are parallel but staggered
27. a short poem, especially a pastoral dialogue
28. to bring out, develop, give rise to
29. exhausted, worn out, incapable
30. shining brilliantly, radiant
31. remarkable, gross, shocking, flagrant
32. either pole of an electric battery
33. the dropping or suppression of a vowel or syllable in or between words
34. to flow forth, issue from, originate
35. profit or salary from office or employment
36. formal or high-flown praise
37. mental weariness from want of occupation or interest
38. short-lived, transitory, lasting only a day or so
39. a short poem with witty ending, a pointed saying
40. an inscription on a tomb
41. an adjective expressing quality or attribute of person or thing
42. a summary, abstract, record in miniature
43. learned, scholarly
44. worthy of esteem or regard
45. to commend, extol, praise
46. to find the amount of, work out the value of
47. to call forth, summon up (spirits, etc.)
48. an explanation, exposition

What Does This Word Mean?
No. 2

49. easily done, working easily, fluent, gentle
50. unnatural, artificial
51. kinds of glazed earthenware and porcelain
52. liable to be deceived or to err, liable to be in error
53. easily disgusted, squeamish
54. fruitful, prolific, fertile
55. a metal ring or cap which strengthens end of a stick, etc.
56. glowing, intense heat, passion, vehemence, zeal
57. a small carved or sculptured figure
58. inclined to split, capable of being split
59. glaring, scandalous
60. generating gas in the stomach, puffed-up, pretentious
61. showing unwanted levity, lacking in gravity or respect
62. like tufts of wool, woolly
63. leaves, leafage
64. to reduce to or express in a formula, set forth systematically
65. accidental, casual, produced by chance
66. refractory, unruly, cross
67. to bear fruit, become fruitful
68. fleeting, evanescent, fugitive
69. to disinfect or purify by means of smoke or fumes, to perfume
70. relating to a funeral, dismal, melancholy, mournful
71. polish up, burnish, renovate, revive
72. a rage, craze or enthusiastic admiration

What Does That Stand For?

A thorough knowledge of the more common abbreviations and symbols is essential nowadays. Where there is more than one possible answer to any of these, give only the most familiar one.

1. A.F.C.	25. F.R.Ċ.S.	49. O.E.D.
2. a.m.	26. F.R.G.S.	50. O.M.
3. A.O.F.	27. G.A.T.T.	51. PAYE
4. A.R.I.B.A.	28. G.C.E.	52. PLUTO
5. B.A.	29. G.E.C.	53. P.P.S.
6. B.E.M.	30. G.M.T.	54. P.T.O.
7. B.O.A.C.	31. H_2O	55. Q.C.
8. B.O.T.	32. Hg	56. R.D.C.
9. B.S.T.	33. H.M.S.O.	57. R.N.L.I.
10. C.H.	34. H.W.M.	58. R.S.V.P.
11. C.I.G.S.	35. I.L.O.	59. S.E.A.T.O.
12. C.M.G.	36. I.Q.	60. S.P.C.K.
13. CO_2	37. I.T.V.	61. STD
14. C.O.I.	38. K.T.	62. TNT
15. C.P.R.E.	39. kWh	63. T.U.C.
16. C.V.O.	40. LL.B.	64. U.A.R.
17. D.D.	41. L.R.C.P.	65. U.N.E.S.C.O.
18. E. and O.E.	42. M.I.C.E.	66. UNICEF
19. E.E.C.	43. Mss.	67. U.P.U.
20. E.F.T.A.	44. M.V.O.	68. U.S.S.R.
21. ERNIE	45. N.A.T.O.	69. V.H.F.
22. F.A.N.Y.	46. N.P.L.	70. V.I.P.
23. F.G.S.	47. N.S.W.	71. W.H.O.
24. F.R.A.M.	48. N.U.R.	72. W.R.N.S.

What Does That Stand For?

1. Air Force Cross
2. *ante meridiem* (before noon)
3. Ancient Order of Foresters
4. Associate of the Royal Institute of British Architects
5. Bachelor of Arts
6. British Empire Medal
7. British Overseas Airways Corporation
8. Board of Trade
9. British summer time
10. Companion of Honour
11. Chief of the Imperial General Staff
12. Companion of the Order of St. Michael and St. George
13. Carbon dioxide
14. Central Office of Information
15. Council for the Protection of Rural England
16. Commander of the Royal Victorian Order
17. Doctor of Divinity
18. Errors and omissions excepted
19. European Economic Community
20. European Free Trade Association
21. Electronic random number indicating equipment
22. First Aid Nursing Yeomanry
23. Fellow of the Geological Society
24. Fellow of the Royal Academy of Music

What Does That Stand For?

25. Fellow of the Royal College of Surgeons
26. Fellow of the Royal Geographical Society
27. General Agreement on Tariffs and Trade
28. General Certificate of Education
29. General Electric Company
30. Greenwich mean time
31. water
32. mercury
33. Her Majesty's Stationery Office
34. High-water mark
35. International Labour Organization
36. intelligence quotient
37. Independent Television
38. Knight of the Order of the Thistle
39. kilowatt hour(s)
40. Bachelor of Laws
41. Licentiate of the Royal College of Physicians
42. Member of the Institution of Civil Engineers
43. manuscripts
44. Member of the Royal Victorian Order
45. North Atlantic Treaty Organization
46. National Physical Laboratory
47. New South Wales
48. National Union of Railwaymen

What Does That Stand For?

49. Oxford English Dictionary
50. Order of Merit
51. pay as you earn
52. pipe-line under the ocean
53. Parliamentary Private Secretary (also *post postscriptum*)
54. please turn over
55. Queen's Counsel
56. Rural District Council
57. Royal National Lifeboat Institution
58. *repondez, s'il vous plait*
59. South-East Asia Treaty Organization
60. Society for the Promotion of Christian Knowledge
61. Subscriber trunk dialling
62. trinitro-toluene
63. Trades Union Congress
64. United Arab Republic
65. United Nations Educational, Scientific and Cultural Organization
66. United Nations Children's Fund
67. Universal Postal Union
68. Union of Soviet Socialist Republics
69. very high frequency
70. very important person
71. World Health Organization
72. Women's Royal Naval Service

How Do You Spell It?

Which of these words are mis-spelt? Give the correct spellings. (Exactly half of them are incorrect).

1. Accomodation
2. Rythm
3. Corroborate
4. Consummate
5. Paralell
6. Indefinible
7. Reprehensible
8. Irelevance
9. Independant
10. Prevalence
11. Presumptuous
12. Delapidated
13. Embarrassed
14. Neccessary
15. Tantalise
16. Permissible
17. Obsolecent
18. Vacilate
19. Ostracize
20. Diarrheoa
21. Serendipity
22. Orrery
23. Immisible
24. Efficacious

25. Picnicing
26. Reconcilable
27. Proceedure
28. Sacriligious
29. Propellor
30. Mischievous
31. Accidently
32. Guarantee
33. Conscientious
34. Benefitted
35. Withhold
36. Blamable
37. Assimmilation
38. Abdomenal
39. Incongruous
40. Collaborate
41. Connoiseur
42. Desicated
43. Hippopotamus
44. Hygeine
45. Inoculate
46. Irridescent
47. Pomegranate
48. Silhouette

49. Supercede
50. Briefly
51. Regretable
52. Imposter
53. Disastrous
54. Predicament
55. Vegetarian
56. Inviegle
57. Reccommend
58. Acknowledge
59. Interminable
60. Subterranean
61. Bachelor
62. Occurence
63. Caterpiller
64. Heterogencous
65. Correlate
66. Diptheria
67. Fullfill
68. Medicinal
69. Vacinate
70. Harrassed
71. Formidable
72. Indestructable

How Do You Spell It?

Here are the correct spellings of the words.

1. Accommodation
2. Rhythm
3. Correct
4. Correct
5. Parallel
6. Indefinable
7. Correct
8. Irrelevance
9. Independent
10. Correct
11. Correct
12. Dilapidated
13. Correct
14. Necessary
15. Correct
16. Correct
17. Obsolescent
18. Vacillate
19. Correct
20. Diarrhoea
21. Correct
22. Correct
23. Immiscible
24. Correct
25. Picnicking
26. Correct
27. Procedure
28. Sacrilegious
29. Propeller
30. Correct
31. Accidentally
32. Correct
33. Correct
34. Benefited
35. Correct
36. Correct
37. Assimilation
38. Abdominal
39. Correct
40. Correct
41. Connoisseur
42. Desiccated
43. Correct
44. Hygiene
45. Correct
46. Iridescent
47. Correct
48. Correct
49. Supersede
50. Correct
51. Regrettable
52. Impostor
53. Correct
54. Correct
55. Correct
56. Inveigle
57. Recommend
58. Correct
59. Correct
60. Correct
61. Correct
62. Occurrence
63. Caterpillar
64. Correct
65. Correct
66. Diphtheria
67. Fulfil
68. Correct
69. Vaccinate
70. Harassed
71. Correct
72. Indestructible

Complete the Word — D

Complete the following words from the given meanings.

1. D . s . . . . l . . not alike
2. D . . . . . y a line of hereditary rulers
3. D . . . s . . n ridicule, mockery
4. D . b . . l . a breaking-up, rout, stampede
5. D . . f . . e . t lacking self-confidence, bashful
6. D . . a . . . c vigorously effective, violent
7. D . . r . s wreckage, accumulated fragments
8. Di . . g . . l . balloon, airship
9. D . m . . c . t . to mark or define the boundary of
10. D . c . . . . t in a state of decay or decline
11. D . . t . r . . y skill, adroitness
12. D . l . . t . . . e lover of the arts, one who toys with a subject
13. D . w . . . r a titled or propertied lady
14. D . s . . l . . e morally lax, licentious
15. D . r . g . t . . . disparaging, detracting from
16. Di . . ip . . . to disperse, scatter, squander
17. D . n . g . . . . to defame, blacken the name of
18. D . . l . v . . . a downward slope
19. D . m . . ee . to tyrannize, be overbearing
20. Do . i . . l . home or residence
21. D . . h . h . . g a union of two vowels pronounced in one syllable
22. D . . . . n . asleep, inactive
23. D . . . l . c . abandoned
24. D . . . i . r . . e tooth-powder

Answers on page 46

Complete the Word — E

Complete the following words from the given meanings.

1. E . p . t . a . . to speak or write at some length
2. E . . r . . e . us external, foreign
3. E . l . c . . c borrowed from various sources, not exclusive
4. E . . g . . a riddle or puzzle
5. E . . n . . c . . t quickly vanishing, fleeting
6. E . . c . r . . t . to embitter, aggravate, irritate
7. E . v . . . n . . n . surrounding area or circumstances
8. El . . . r . t . to work out in detail, enlarge upon
9. E . qu . . . t . that which arouses great admiration, acute
10. E . . ul . . t . ornamental shoulder-piece of a uniform
11. E . f . . v . . c . to give off gaseous bubbles
12. E . v . s . . e to face or contemplate
13. E . . e . e . l light, airy, spirit-like
14. E . . rv . . . to weaken
15. E . i . . e fit to be eaten
16. E . b . . z . . to divert money to one's own use fraudulently
17. E . . i . c . that which has died out
18. E . . on . . . s mistaken, incorrect
19. E . . l . . nt flowing out
20. E . c . . p . t . to free from blame, exonerate
21. En . . . st . . painting by burning in
22. E . . l . g . . a speech or poem at the end of a play
23. E . . . r a young eel
24. Ex . . e . . v . an oath or exclamation

Answers on page 46

Complete the Word — F

Complete the following words from the given meanings.

1. F..t.t...s not real, counterfeit, imaginary
2. F.r.c.o.. fierce, savage, cruel
3. F.n.s.. artfulness, delicate manipulation
4. F.o..s...t flowering
5. F..n..y servant or footman
6. F...c...r type of cable railway
7. F..u.u. silly, idiotic
8. Fo...d..le hard to overcome or defeat
9. F.l..f. misrepresent, alter
10. F...b..g..t.. dumbfounded, astonished
11. F..m..t something invented or imagined
12. F....g.n... containing iron
13. F.u..l careful, sparing
14. F.l.c...us apt, happy in manner
15. F.r.b..i.. an omen or presentiment
16. Fr...r...e to associate or make friends with
17. F.b..c.t. to invent or 'make up'
18. F..s.r. a cleft or narrow opening
19. F.u.t... enjoyment from possession or realization of something
20. F..eti..s waggish, jocular
21. F..t..l. a fleet of boats
22. F..v.l... paltry, trifling, not serious
23. F.r..t..e courage in adversity
24. F..x..l. pliable, supple, adaptable

Complete the Word

D	E	F
1. Dissimilar	1. Expatiate	1. Fictitious
2. Dynasty	2. Extraneous	2. Ferocious
3. Derision	3. Eclectic	3. Finesse
4. Débâcle	4. Enigma	4. Florescent
5. Diffident	5. Evanescent	5. Flunkey
6. Drastic	6. Exacerbate	6. Funicular
7. Debris	7. Environment	7. Fatuous
8. Dirigible	8. Elaborate	8. Formidable
9. Demarcate	9. Exquisite	9. Falsify
10. Decadent	10. Epaulette	10. Flabbergasted
11. Dexterity	11. Effervesce	11. Figment
12. Dilettante	12. Envisage	12. Ferruginous
13. Dowager	13. Ethereal	13. Frugal
14. Dissolute	14. Enervate	14. Felicitous
15. Derogatory	15. Edible	15. Foreboding
16. Dissipate	16. Embezzle	16. Fraternize
17. Denigrate	17. Extinct	17. Fabricate
18. Declivity	18. Erroneous	18. Fissure
19. Domineer	19. Effluent	19. Fruition
20. Domicile	20. Exculpate	20. Facetious
21. Diphthong	21. Encaustic	21. Flotilla
22. Dormant	22. Epilogue	22. Frivolous
23. Derelict	23. Elver	23. Fortitude
24. Dentifrice	24. Expletive	24. Flexible

What's in a Name?

Everybody likes to know the meaning of his or her name and home town, but what about the names of other people and places? Do you know the meanings of these names?

Christian names	Surnames	Place names
1. Charles	1. Barker	1. Birmingham
2. Edward	2. Barton	2. Bradford
3. George	3. Bowen	3. Bristol
4. Jeremy	4. Brown	4. Buxton
5. John	5. Chapman	5. Cardiff
6. Paul	6. Davis	6. Derby
7. Peter	7. Elliot	7. Durham
8. Richard	8. Evans	8. Edinburgh
9. Robert	9. Green	9. Ely
10. Stephen	10. Hill	10. Glasgow
11. Thomas	11. Higginbotham	11. Jarrow
12. William	12. Jones	12. Leighton
13. Anne	13. Kemp	Buzzard
14. Barbara	14. Lambert	13. Lewes
15. Deborah	15. MacIntosh	14. London
16. Dorothy	16. Nicholls	15. Manchester
17. Elizabeth	17. Price	16. Melton
18. Joan	18. Robinson	Mowbray
19. Louise	19. Scott	17. Norwich
20. Margaret	20. Shaw	18. Oswaldtwistle
21. Mary	21. Smith	19. Pembroke
22. Patricia	22. Taylor	20. Pontefract
23. Sarah	23. Walker	21. Pwllheli
24. Susan	24. Wright	22. Sheffield
		23. Southampton
		24. Winchester

Answers page 49

Answers page 50

What's in a Name?

Christian Names

1. Charles = 'a man' (from German *Karl* and Latin *Carolus*).
2. Edward = 'rich or happy guardian' (from A-Saxon).
3. George = 'farmer or tiller of the soil' (Greek *georgos*).
4. Jeremy = 'God has appointed or exalted' (from Hebrew)
5. John = 'God is gracious' or 'God has favoured' (from Hebrew).
6. Paul = 'small' (from Latin *paulus*).
7. Peter = 'a stone' (from Greek *petros*).
8. Richard = 'a hard ruler or king' (from Old German).
9. Robert = 'bright fame' (from Old German).
10. Stephen = 'a garland or crown' (Greek *Stephanos*).
11. Thomas = 'a twin' (from Aramaic)
12. William = 'will' + 'helmet' (Old German *Willahelm*).
13. Anne = 'grace' (from Greek *Anna* and Hebrew *Hannah*).
14. Barbara = 'a stranger' (from Greek *barbaros*).
15. Deborah = 'a bee' (from Hebrew).
16. Dorothy = 'a gift of God' (from Greek).
17. Elizabeth = 'consecrated to God' (from Hebrew).
18. Joan, Jean or Jane = 'God is gracious' (from Hebrew).
19. Louise = 'famous war' (from French *Louis* and Old German).
20. Margaret = 'a pearl' (Latin *margarita*).
21. Mary = 'plump, fat' (from Hebrew).
22. Patricia = feminine form of Patrick (Latin 'a nobleman').
23. Sarah = 'quarrelsome', later meaning 'a princess' (Hebrew).
24. Susan = 'graceful lily' (Hebrew *Susanna*).

What's in a Name?

Surnames   O.E. = Old English

1. Barker = 'a tanner' (Old Norse) or 'a shepherd' (Old French).
2. Barton = 'barley farm' (O.E.).
3. Bowen = 'son of Owen' (Welsh).
4. Brown = 'brown-haired or brown-skinned' (O.E.).
5. Chapman = 'merchant, trader' (O.E. *cheap-man*).
6. Davis, Davies = 'son of David' (Welsh).
7. Elliot = 'Jehovah is God' (from Greek *Elias* and Hebrew *Elijah*).
8. Evans = 'son of Evan' (one of the Welsh forms of John).
9. Green = '(village) green' (O.E.).
10. Hill = 'a hill' (O.E.).
11. Higginbotham = 'a valley with oaks' (O.E.).
12. Jones = 'son of John' (Welsh *Ioan*).
13. Kemp = 'warrior, champion' (O.E.).
14. Lambert = 'land-bright' (Old German).
15. MacIntosh = 'son of the chieftain' (Gaelic).
16. Nicholls = 'son of Nicholas'.
17. Price = 'son of Rhys' (Welsh).
18. Robinson, Robertson = 'son of Robert'.
19. Scott = from 'the Scots'.
20. Shaw = 'a copse or small wood' (O.E.).
21. Smith = 'blacksmith, metal-worker, etc.' (O.E.).
22. Taylor = 'a cutter' (Old French *tailor*).
23. Walker = 'a fuller' (O.E.).
24. Wright = 'a carpenter, joiner or craftsman' (O.E.).

What's in a Name?

Place names

1. Birmingham = 'the village of Beorma's or Beornmund's people'.
2. Bradford = 'broad ford'.
3. Bristol = 'place near, or site of, the bridge' (O.E. *Brycgstow*).
4. Buxton = 'rocking stones' (O.E. *buchestanes*).
5. Cardiff = 'fort on the River Taf(f)'.
6. Derby = 'village with deer or deer-park' (Scand. *Deoraby*).
7. Durham = 'island with a hill' (O.E. *Dunholm*).
8. Edinburgh = 'the fortress Eidyn'.
9. Ely = 'eel district' (O.E. *Elge*).
10. Glasgow = 'green hollow'.
11. Jarrow = 'the Gyrwe or fen people' (O.E. *Gyruum*).
12. Leighton Buzzard = 'a leek-garden' + Buzzard (a family name).
13. Lewes = 'hills' (O.E. *hlaew*).
14. London = 'place belonging to Londinos' (Celtic).
15. Manchester = Old Brit. *Mamucion* + *ceaster* = 'Roman town'.
16. Melton Mowbray = 'middle farm' (of Roger de Moubray).
17. Norwich = 'north port or town' (Saxon *Norowic*).
18. Oswaldtwistle = 'tongue of land belonging to Oswald' (O.E. *twisla* = river-fork).
19. Pembroke = 'end land'.
20. Pontefract = 'broken bridge' (from Latin and French).
21. Pwllheli = 'salt pool'.
22. Sheffield = 'open land by the river Sheaf'.
23. Southampton = 'village on a meadow or river-land'.
24. Winchester = 'Roman town called *Venta*' + *ceaster* = 'Roman town'.

Singular and Plural

What is the plural of each of these words?

1. Thief
2. Dwarf
3. City
4. Chimney
5. Folio
6. Analysis
7. Hero
8. Larva
9. Seraph
10. Bison
11. Self
12. Roof
13. Cargo
14. Focus
15. Radius
16. Handful
17. Man-servant
18. Brother-in-law
19. Ignoramus
20. Tomato
21. Court martial
22. Index
23. Axis
24. Sphinx
25. Nebula
26. Crisis
27. Phenomenon
28. Nucleus
29. Cherub
30. Chrysalis
31. Stratum
32. Octopus
33. Graffito
34. Formula
35. Bureau
36. Stimulus

What is the singular of each of these words?

1. Bacteria
2. Agenda
3. Moose
4. Lice
5. Data
6. Alumni
7. Series
8. Genera

Singular and Plural

1. Thieves
2. Dwarfs
3. Cities
4. Chimneys
5. Folios
6. Analyses
7. Heroes
8. Larvae
9. Seraphs or seraphim
10. Bison
11. Selves
12. Roofs
13. Cargoes
14. Foci or focuses
15. Radii
16. Handfuls
17. Men-servants
18. Brothers-in-law
19. Ignoramuses
20. Tomatoes
21. Courts martial
22. Indexes or indices
23. Axes
24. Sphinxes or sphinges
25. Nebulae
26. Crises
27. Phenomena
28. Nuclei or nucleuses
29. Cherubs or cherubim
30. Chrysalises or chrysalides
31. Strata
32. Octopuses or octopodes
33. Graffiti
34. Formulae or formulas
35. Bureaus or bureaux
36. Stimuli

*　　*　　*

1. Bacterium
2. Agendum
3. Moose
4. Louse
5. Datum
6. Alumnus
7. Series
8. Genus

What Does This Word Mean?
No. 3

Give the meanings of these words.

1. Galaxy	25. Habituate	49. Iconoclast
2. Gallimaufry	26. Haematite	50. Idiosyncrasy
3. Galore	27. Haggard	51. Ignominy
4. Gambit	28. Hallucination	52. Ignoramus
5. Garish	29. Harass	53. Illimitable
6. Garniture	30. Hastate	54. Imbroglio
7. Garrulous	31. Hedonism	55. Immanent
8. Gauche	32. Heinous	56. Immure
9. Genealogy	33. Hemlock	57. Impale
10. Genteel	34. Hereditament	58. Impasse
11. Genuflect	35. Heterogeneous	59. Impecunious
12. Gibberish	36. Hiatus	60. Imperturbable
13. Gingerly	37. Hirsute	61. Incarcerated
14. Glaciated	38. Homily	62. Inchoate
15. Glandiferous	39. Homogeneous	63. Indigenous
16. Gorgeous	40. Hone	64. Ineluctable
17. Grandeur	41. Honorarium	65. Infringe
18. Gratuitous	42. Horripilation	66. Inimical
19. Gregarious	43. Howitzer	67. Integument
20. Grotto	44. Humid	68. Interpolate
21. Guillemot	45. Hydropathy	69. Inveterate
22. Gumption	46. Hyphen	70. Inviolate
23. Gymkhana	47. Hypochondriac	71. Irascible
24. Gyrate	48. Hypotenuse	72. Irrevocable

What Does This Word Mean?
No. 3

1. a luminous band of stars, a crowd of distinguished people
2. a mixture, jumble, medley
3. in plenty or abundance
4. an opening move, especially in a game of chess
5. obtrusively or excessively bright, showy, gaudy
6. appurtenances, adornment, trimming, dressing
7. loquacious, wordy
8. awkward, clumsy
9. the study of pedigrees, tracing of person's ancestors
10. well-dressed, elegant, characteristics of upper classes
11. to kneel or bend the knee
12. unintelligible speech, jargon
13. cautiously, timidly
14. marked, polished or eroded by ice action, covered by glaciers
15. bearing acorns or similar fruit
16. richly coloured, magnificent, showy, dazzling
17. great power, majesty, splendour of living
18. freely given or obtained, uncalled for, unjustifiable
19. living in flocks or communities, fond of company
20. a picturesque cave or cavern, often artificial
21. a species of sea-birds
22. common sense, shrewdness, resource, a vehicle for colour (painting)
23. an athletic-sports display, a place for such a display
24. to move in a circle, revolve, whirl

What Does This Word Mean?
No. 3

25. to fix in a habit, to accustom to
26. an iron ore
27. (of a person) wild-looking, gaunt: (of a hawk) wild, untamed
28. an illusion, the perception of an object not actually present
29. to vex, trouble, worry, wear out or exhaust
30. spear-shaped
31. the doctrine that pleasure is the chief good
32. infamous, atrocious, highly criminal
33. a poisonous plant
34. property that can be inherited, real property, inheritance
35. diverse in character, of diverse elements
36. a break or gap in a series or chain, or between two vowels
37. relating to hair, hairy, shaggy
38. a sermon, lecture, tedious moralizing discourse
39. of the same kind, alike, similar, uniform
40. a stone for sharpening tools
41. an honorary reward, fee for services rendered
42. creeping of the flesh, 'goose-flesh'
43. a gun which fires heavy shells
44. moist, damp
45. medical treatment by application of water
46. a dash used to connect two words
47. depression without cause, or by unfounded belief of bodily disease
48. the side opposite the right angle of a triangle

What Does This Word Mean?
No. 3

49. a breaker of images, one who attacks cherished beliefs
50. mental constitution peculiar to a person, individual bent
51. dishonour, disgrace, infamy
52. an ignorant person
53. that which has no limits, boundless
54. confused heap, complicated situation, misunderstanding
55. indwelling, inherent
56. to imprison, confine within walls, shut oneself up
57. to thrust a stake through
58. a blind alley, a way with no outlet
59. penniless, in need of money
60. not excitable, serene, calm
61. imprisoned, confined
62. undeveloped, immature, just begun; (*verb*) to begin
63. native, belonging naturally, innate
64. inescapable
65. to break or violate, to contravene
66. unfriendly or hostile to, harmful
67. a skin, husk, shell, natural covering of animal or plant
68. to make insertions (in books, etc.), introduce or insert terms
69. long-established, deep-rooted, hardened, settled, obstinate
70. unhurt, unbroken, unprofaned, not violated
71. prone to anger, irritable, choleric
72. unalterable, irreversible, beyond recall

Rare Words

Many words are seldom used in everyday language. Here are some of these uncommon words; most of them however have simpler and more straightforward meanings than many common words. If you get six or more correct, give yourself a pat on the back!

1. Adipescent
2. Aduncous
3. Albescent
4. Ammophilous
5. Atimy
6. Bibacious
7. Buccinatory
8. Calcariform
9. Cataplexy
10. Cespitose
11. Chiaroscuro
12. Chironomy
13. Cicatrice
14. Clepsydra
15. Contabescent
16. Crepuscular
17. Deliquescence
18. Divarication
19. Eccaleobion
20. Edentate
21. Eleemosynary
22. Epalpebrate
23. Epistaxis
24. Fellifluous
25. Fimbriated
26. Fissiparous
27. Funiform
28. Geophagist
29. Glossologist
30. Gummous
31. Hagiolatry
32. Hecatomb
33. Homodont
34. Ianthine
35. Idiograph
36. Immiscible
37. Impudicity
38. Incalescent
39. Incondite
40. Lactifluous
41. Latifoliate
42. Lucifugous
43. Monoculous
44. Multiloquence
45. Nephrotomy
46. Nuncupate
47. Obfuscate
48. Obliviscence
49. Pentadactyl
50. Peristeronic
51. Plumiform
52. Polyonymous
53. Revirescence
54. Rhyparographer
55. Sciopticon
56. Securiform
57. Senocular
58. Sternutation
59. Strabismus
60. Strigose
61. Supellectile
62. Tabescent
63. Tephromancy
64. Tenebrosity
65. Tralatitious
66. Triphthong
67. Urticate
68. Uxoricide
69. Vespertine
70. Vicegerent
71. Volitate
72. Zymurgy

Rare Words

1. becoming fatty
2. hooked, curved inward
3. growing or passing into white
4. sand-loving
5. public disgrace
6. given to drinking
7. pertaining to a trumpeter or trumpeting
8. shaped like a spur
9. the hypnotic state in animals when they 'sham dead'
10. growing in tufts or clumps, turfy
11. the disposition of light and shade in a painting
12. the art of gesticulation in oratory
13. the scar of a healed wound
14. an ancient type of water-clock
15. wasting away, atrophied
16. pertaining to twilight, dim, indistinct
17. melting away, becoming liquid
18. the action of stretching apart, spreading out, divergence
19. an egg-hatching apparatus
20. without front teeth
21. relating to or supported by alms or alms-giving
22. having no eyebrows
23. bleeding from the nose
24. flowing with gall

Rare Words

25. having a border or fringe
26. reproducing by fission
27. having the form of a rope or cord
28. a person who eats earth
29. one who defines terms, one versed in the science of language
30. of the nature of gum, gum-like
31. the worship of saints
32. a great public sacrifice
33. having teeth all of the same kind
34. violet-coloured
35. a person's private mark or signature
36. incapable of mixture e.g. water and oil
37. shamelessness, immodesty
38. increasing in warmth
39. ill constructed, crude, unpolished
40. flowing with milk
41. having broad leaves
42. shunning the light
43. one-eyed
44. given to much talking
45. surgical incision of the kidney
46. to declare a will orally
47. to darken, obscure, bewilder
48. forgetfulness

Rare Words

49. having five toes or fingers
50. pertaining to pigeons
51. feather-shaped
52. having several different names or titles
53. return to a youthful or flourishing state
54. a painter of mean or sordid subjects
55. a type of magic lantern
56. axe-shaped
57. having six eyes
58. the action of sneezing; a sneeze
59. an affliction of the eyes causing a squint
60. covered with stiff hairs
61. pertaining to household furniture; ornamental
62. wasting away
63. divination by means of ashes
64. darkness, obscurity
65. relating to transference of words, metaphorical; handed down or traditional
66. a combination of three vowel sounds in one syllable
67. to sting like a nettle
68. the murder of one's wife
69. relating to the evening; taking place in the evening
70. one who exercises delegated power; a deputy
71. to fly with a fluttering motion
72. the practice of fermentation

From Far and Wide

Can you say from which language or country each of these words comes? Some are borrowed from foreign languages, some are derived from Greek and Latin and a few are from Old English

1. Limousine	25. Kayak	49. Cigar
2. Bravado	26. Lemming	50. Coffee
3. Verandah	27. Assassin	51. Caddy
4. Piano	28. Kimono	52. Taffrail
5. Steppe	29. Census	53. Jungle
6. Yacht	30. Horde	54. Alphabet
7. Plunder	31. Ombudsman	55. Minaret
8. Kiwi	32. Parasol	56. Rickshaw
9. Paddy	33. Chimpanzee	57. Sherbet
10. Tea	34. Bazaar	58. Mistletoe
11. Tycoon	35. Scenario	59. Puncture
12. Goulash	36. Parallax	60. Hammock
13. Bungalow	37. Fuselage	61. Chassis
14. Algebra	38. Cherub	62. Iceberg
15. Divan	39. Twenty	63. Geodesy
16. Kiosk	40. Cafeteria	64. Skipper
17. Floe	41. Bantam	65. Manifesto
18. Gauntlet	42. Poltergeist	66. Radius
19. Tattoo	43. Ketchup	67. Nadir
20. Igloo	44. Schooner	68. Canoe
21. Totem	45. Khaki	69. Typhoon
22. Premium	46. Vodka	70. Rendezvous
23. Robot	47. Elastic	71. Bamboo
24. Whisky	48. Hollow	72. Balcony

From Far and Wide

1. French
2. Spanish
3. Portuguese
4. Italian
5. Russian
6. Dutch
7. German
8. Maori
9. Malay
10. Chinese
11. Japanese
12. Magyar (Hungary)
13. Hindustani
14. Arabic
15. Persian
16. Turkish
17. Norse
18. Swedish
19. Polynesian
20. Eskimo
21. North American Indian
22. Latin
23. Czech
24. Celtic (Gaelic)

25. Eskimo
26. Norwegian
27. Arabic
28. Japanese
29. Latin
30. Turkish
31. Swedish
32. Italian
33. West Africa
34. Persian
35. Italian
36. Greek
37. French
38. Hebrew
39. Old English
40. Spanish
41. Malay
42. German
43. Chinese
44. Dutch
45. Hindustani
46. Russian
47. Greek
48. Old English

49. Spanish
50. Arabic via Turkish
51. Malay
52. Dutch
53. Hindi
54. Greek
55. Arabic
56. Japanese
57. Arabic
58. Old English
59. Latin
60. Spanish
61. French
62. German
63. Greek
64. Dutch
65. Italian
66. Latin
67. Arabic
68. Haytian via Spanish
69. Chinese
70. French
71. Malay
72. Italian

Complete the Word — G

Complete the following words from the given meanings.

1. Gn . . s .   a type of rock
2. G . . . t . n . . s   jelly-like
3. G . as . l .   horrible, frightful
4. G . . m . . . t .   to sprout or bud
5. G . . d . . . t   degree of slope
6. G . . f . .   coarse laughter
7. G . . n . s .   to decorate, embellish
8. G . r . . n . . . n   enormous, gigantic
9. G . . b . . .   convex, hump-shaped
10. G . . . l . n   imaginary mischievous sprite or elf
11. G . . . o . a   type of boat
12. G . l . . n . t .   type of explosive
13. Gn . . l . .   twisted, rugged, knobbly
14. G . . b . . .   a small round drop (of liquid)
15. G . w . .   awkward, ungainly
16. G . . . r . . . y   the art of good eating
17. G . . . . a . .   one who has a degree
18. G . . f . . t .   writing scratched on walls
19. Go . . . m . .   a filmy substance made of spiders' webs
20. G . . e . te . .   a geographical dictionary
21. G . r . a . .   relevant or pertinent
22. G . s . . c . l . . .   to motion or gesture with the limbs
23. Gl . . . . . y   a list of words or dictionary
24. G . u . o . .   a type of sugar

Answers on page 66

Complete the Word — H

Complete the following words from the given meanings.

1. H . . . . d . . s risky, perilous
2. H . . e . . s repulsive, revolting
3. H . . t . l . . . antagonism, opposition
4. H . l . . . l spiral
5. H . r . . . r place of shelter
6. Ha . . n . . e to address or speak loudly and vehemently
7. H . l . . . d a combined spear and battle-axe
8. H . . i . o . . e. a kind of aircraft
9. H . e . o . . . p . . c an ancient form of writing
10. H . . s . . . d old liquid measure
11. H . p . a . . r . chance, random
12. H . . . c . . s. pretence, simulation of virtue
13. H . . i . . t . . . indecision, reluctance
14. H . . i . . d . the killing of a human being
15. H . . ch . . . t escutcheon, armorial shield
16. H . l . c . . . t wholesale destruction or slaughter
17. H . . . r . ou . mirthful, joyous
18. H . . . . n . . e to sleep through the winter
19. H . . m . . i . . s agreeable, concordant
20. H . . d . . . g precipitate, impetuous
21. H . . . o . . type of hanging bed
22. H . n . . . n . . obstruction, obstacle
23. H . b . . d offspring of two different species
24. H . . e . s . . . type of canvas carrying-bag

Answers on page 66

Complete the Word — I

Complete the following words from the given meanings.

1. I . m . . . l . t .   pure, spotless, faultless
2. I . c . . s . . t   unceasing, continual
3. I . . r . d . c . . . .   that which cannot be got rid of
4. I . . n . . . r .   a route or guide-book
5. I . . . st . . . us   distinguished, famous
6. In . . . s . . . r . . .   thoughtless, regardless of others
7. In . . . n . . g . . t   uncompromising, unmoved
8. I . m . . ab . .   unalterable, unchangeable
9. I . . . n . r . . .   to burn, reduce to ashes
10. I . l . s . . e   deceptive
11. I . s . . s . . .   unfeeling, without sensation
12. I . . or . . . . te   persistent, pressing
13. I . . . b . . .   motionless
14. I . . l . . . . b . .   easily set on fire
15. I . . r . . c . l . . .   not jointed, unable to speak clearly
16. I . m . n . . .   impending, soon to occur
17. In . . d . . i . . .   unwise, ill-judged
18. I . g . . t . . . .   to get oneself into favour with
19. I . p . . c . . l .   faultless
20. I . s . . . d   tasteless, lifeless
21. I . . u . . . d . n . . .   disobedient, rebellious
22. I . . . m . t . . l .   unyielding, stubborn
23. I . v . . . l .   to entice or seduce
24. I . . er . ec . . . .   a fault or blemish

Complete the Word

G	H	I
1. Gneiss	1. Hazardous	1. Immaculate
2. Gelatinous	2. Hideous	2. Incessant
3. Ghastly	3. Hostility	3. Ineradicable
4. Germinate	4. Helical	4. Itinerary
5. Gradient	5. Harbour	5. Illustrious
6. Guffaw	6. Harangue	6. Inconsiderate
7. Garnish	7. Halberd	7. Intransigent
8. Gargantuan	8. Helicopter	8. Immutable
9. Gibbous	9. Hieroglyphic	9. Incinerate
10. Gremlin	10. Hogshead	10. Illusive
11. Gondola	11. Haphazard	11. Insensate
12. Gelignite	12. Hypocrisy	12. Importunate
13. Gnarled	13. Hesitation	13. Immobile
14. Globule	14. Homicide	14. Inflammable
15. Gawky	15. Hatchment	15. Inarticulate
16. Gastronomy	16. Holocaust	16. Imminent
17. Graduate	17. Hilarious	17. Injudicious
18. Graffiti	18. Hibernate	18. Ingratiate
19. Gossamer	19. Harmonious	19. Impeccable
20. Gazetteer	20. Headlong	20. Insipid
21. Germane	21. Hammock	21. Insubordinate
22. Gesticulate	22. Hindrance	22. Indomitable
23. Glossary	23. Hybrid	23. Inveigle
24. Glucose	24. Haversack	24. Imperfection

Back to School!

Give the meanings of these words, all of which you may come across in the course of normal reading.

Geography and Geology	Biology, Botany and Zoology	Chemistry, Maths, and Physics
1. Anticyclone	1. Aorta	1. Asteroid
2. Archipelago	2. Carnivore	2. Astigmatism
3. Basalt	3. Cartilage	3. Barbiturate
4. Col	4. Chlorophyll	4. Bronze
5. Delta	5. Chromosomes	5. Casein
6. Drumlin	6. Clavicle	6. Cathode
7. Equinox	7. Coniferous	7. Erg
8. Fiord	8. Deciduous	8. Fluoridation
9. Glacier	9. Epidermis	9. Halogen
10. Isobar	10. Gene	10. Integer
11. Isthmus	11. Haemoglobin	11. Isosceles
12. Lava	12. Hormone	12. Light-year
13. Meridian	13. Latex	13. Methane
14. Monsoon	14. Metabolism	14. Micron
15. Moraine	15. Mollusc	15. Myopia
16. Orthomorphic	16. Penicillin	16. Ozone
17. Rhumb-line	17. Plankton	17. Polaroid
18. Scarp	18. Plasma	18. Polygon
19. Scree	19. Pollen	19. Refraction
20. Solstice	20. Protoplasm	20. Specific gravity
21. Stalactite	21. Stamen	21. Spectroscope
22. Theodolite	22. Tendril	22. Surd
23. Tundra	23. Tuber	23. Tangent
24. Watershed	24. Vitamin	24. Torque

Back to School!

Geography and Geology

1. an area of relatively high pressure, with settled weather
2. a scattered group of islands
3. a type of volcanic rock (the Giant's Causeway is basalt)
4. a depression or low point in a mountain range, providing a pass across
5. an alluvial area at the mouth of a river
6. a low, elongated hill formed of material deposited by a glacier
7. the time of the year when the sun is directly overhead at noon at the Equator
8. a long, deep, narrow inlet of the sea (as in Norway)
9. a large mass of ice moving slowly down a valley
10. a line on a map joining places with equal barometric pressure
11. a neck of land connecting two land areas, with water either side
12. molten rock which has solidified on the earth's surface
13. a line of Longitude
14. the seasonal winds in south-east Asia, also the rains which accompany these winds
15. the material deposited by a glacier
16. a type of map projection which preserves the shape of small areas
17. a line of constant bearing, cutting meridians at the same angle
18. the steep slope of a line of hills or ridge
19. a mass of boulders and stones which lies at the foot of a hill
20. the time of the year when the sun is directly overhead at the Tropics
21. a column of calcium carbonate hanging from the roof of a limestone cave
22. a surveying instrument used for measuring angles
23. the treeless plains of the subarctic regions
24. the line which separates streams flowing into different river basins

Back to School!

Biology, Botany and Zoology ·

1. the large artery leading from the left ventricle of the heart
2. a flesh-eating mammal
3. the skeletal tissue in vertebrate animals
4. the green colouring matter in the cells of plants
5. small bodies in the nuclei of living cells
6. the collar-bone of a human
7. the type of trees which produce cones
8. the trees which shed their leaves every year
9. the outer layer of the skin of animals
10. a unit of inherited material or a hereditary factor
11. the pigment in the blood of vertebrates and a few other animals
12. a chemical substance produced by certain glands
13. a milky fluid produced by some plants and trees e.g. rubber
14. the chemical processes or changes occurring within an organism
15. an animal with a hard shell e.g. oyster, snail
16. an antibiotic obtained from a vegetable mould
17. microscopic animal and plant life near the surface of lake or sea
18. the liquid in which blood corpuscles float
19. the spores of plants
20. the living material of the cells of all organisms
21. the stalk-shaped organ of a flower which produces pollen
22. a modified stem or leaf which a plant uses for support
23. an underground root or stem, swollen with stored food
24. an organic substance found in many foods and necessary for life

Back to School!

Chemistry, Maths and Physics

1. a small planet orbiting round the sun
2. a defect in the lens of the eye
3. a drug made from barbituric acid, given to promote sleep
4. an alloy of copper and tin
5. the protein found in milk (cheese is mainly casein)
6. a negative electrical plate or electrode
7. a unit of work or energy
8. the adding of fluoride to drinking water
9. any one of these four elements: fluorine, iodine, bromine, chlorine
10. any whole number e.g. 15, 6, 100 (*not* e.g. $3\frac{1}{2}$)
11. a triangle with two sides or two angles equal
12. the distance travelled by light in one year
13. a compound of hydrogen and carbon, also called marsh gas or fire-damp
14. a thousandth part of a millimetre
15. short-sightedness
16. a form of oxygen (O_3) produced by passing electricity through the air
17. a material used to produce polarized light
18. a geometrical figure with more than four sides and angles
19. the bending of a ray of light when passing from one substance to another
20. the relation between the weight of any substance and the weight of water
21. an instrument for producing and observing the spectrum
22. a number, especially a square root, which cannot be expressed exactly
23. a line touching a circle or curve at a point without cutting it
24. the turning or twisting force in a body tending to cause rotation

Who Are the Rulers?

The suffix '-*cracy*' comes from a Greek word meaning 'power' or 'rule'; an 'o' was later added to form the familiar ending '-*ocracy*', and it was used as a nonce-word (i.e. a temporary word) to mean rule by any particular class; e.g. '*aristocracy*' means 'rule by noblemen'. The suffix '-*archy*' is also derived from a Greek word meaning 'to rule'; e.g. '*oligarchy*' means 'rule by the few'. Who are the rulers in the following systems?

1. Autocracy
2. Bureaucracy
3. Democracy
4. Dulocracy
5. Gerontocracy
6. Kakistocracy
7. Monocracy
8. Pantisocracy
9. Plutocracy
10. Ptochocracy
11. Stratocracy
12. Theocracy
13. Anarchy
14. Decadarchy
15. Gynarchy
16. Hagiarchy
17. Hecatontarchy
18. Heptarchy
19. Matriarchy
20. Monarchy
21. Octarchy
22. Patriarchy
23. Pentarchy
24. Triarchy

Who are or were the following rulers?

25. Sultan
26. Nabob
27. Nizam
28. Ameer, Amir or Emir
29. Doge
30. Shah

Who Are the Rulers?

1. Rule by: absolute authority, a ruler with absolute power
2. officials
3. the people
4. slaves
5. old men
6. the worst citizens
7. one person
8. everybody (all are equal)
9. the rich
10. the poor
11. the military
12. a deity or God
13. nobody – it means an absence of government
14. ten persons
15. a woman or women
16. priests or saints
17. a hundred persons
18. seven persons
19. the mother as the head of the family
20. a king or queen
21. eight persons
22. the father or founder, or head of a Church
23. five persons
24. three persons
25. sovereign of a Mohammedan country, especially Turkey
26. governor of an Indian district
27. hereditary ruler of Hyderabad
28. Mohammedan ruler of Sind and Afghanistan
29. chief magistrate in the Republics of Venice and Genoa
30. King of Persia

What Does This Word Mean? No. 4

Give the meanings of these words.

1. Lackadaisical	25. Machinate	49. Naïve
2. Lampoon	26. Magnanimous	50. Narcissism
3. Languid	27. Maladroit	51. Natation
4. Lectern	28. Maleficent	52. Nebulous
5. Leeward	29. Marquee	53. Necromancy
6. Legerdemain	30. Masticate	54. Nefarious
7. Lentitude	31. Mellifluous	55. Negate
8. Lethargy	32. Mendacious	56. Negligible
9. Lexicography	33. Mercurial	57. Neophyte
10. Ligeous	34. Meretricious	58. Nephology
11. Limbo	35. Meticulous	59. Nescient
12. Limpid	36. Minatory	60. Nexus
13. Lineage	37. Mischance	61. Nidificate
14. Lissom	38. Misogynist	62. Niggardly
15. Lithium	39. Mitigate	63. Nomenclature
16. Litigate	40. Modulate	64. Nonchalant
17. Loggia	41. Monitory	65. Nonpareil
18. Loquacious	42. Mordant	66. Nostalgia
19. Loxodrome	43. Moribund	67. Nostrum
20. Lucid	44. Multifarious	68. Notional
21. Lugubrious	45. Munificent	69. Novercal
22. Lunate	46. Muslin	70. Nuance
23. Lusty	47. Mutilate	71. Nugatory
24. Luxuriate	48. Myriad	72. Nullify

Answers page 75   Answers page 76

What Does This Word Mean? No. 4

1. languishing, feebly sentimental
2. a virulent or scurrilous satire, to write such
3. inert, spiritless, apathetic, dull, sluggish, faint, weak
4. a reading- or singing-desk in a church
5. away from or on the sheltered side of the wind
6. sleight of hand, conjuring tricks, jugglery
7. slowness, sluggishness
8. drowsiness or prolonged sleep, torpor, inertness, apathy
9. the writing or compilation of a dictionary
10. (of plants) like wood, woody
11. unfavourable place or condition of neglect, prison, oblivion
12. clear, pellucid, not turbid
13. ancestry, pedigree, lineal descent
14. supple, agile, lithesome
15. a metallic element
16. to go to law, contest, dispute
17. a gallery or arcade with one or more sides open to the air
18. talkative, wordy
19. a line on the earth cutting all meridians at same angle
20. clear, intelligible
21. mournful, doleful, dismal
22. crescent-shaped
23. vigorous, strong, lively
24. enjoy oneself, revel, indulge in luxury

What Does This Word Mean?
No. 4

25. to lay plots, intrigue, scheme
26. high-souled, above petty feelings or conduct
27. awkward, bungling, lacking in adroitness
28. doing harm or wrong, hurtful, criminal
29. a large tent
30. to grind with the teeth, chew
31. as sweet as honey
32. lying, untruthful, false
33. sprightly, volatile, ready-witted, of or containing mercury
34. showily attractive, befitting a harlot
35. over-careful about small details
36. threatening, menacing
37. piece of bad luck, ill-luck, mishap
38. a hater of women
39. to alleviate, appease, moderate
40. to regulate, adjust, attune, vary tone of
41. giving warning, admonitory
42. caustic, biting, corrosive
43. at the point of death, dying
44. having great variety, many and various
45. splendidly generous, bountiful
46. a delicately-woven cotton fabric
47. to cut off, destroy, or render imperfect by removing limb or other part
48. countless, innumerable

What Does This Word Mean?
No. 4

49. unsophisticated, artless
50. self-love, self-admiration
51. the action or art of swimming
52. cloudy, hazy, vague, formless, like a nebula
53. art of prediction by communication with the dead, magic
54. wicked, iniquitous, villainous
55. to deny or nullify
56. that which can be disregarded or neglected
57. a new convert, novice, beginner
58. the study of clouds
59. ignorant of, agnostic
60. a bond, link, connexion, connected group
61. to make a nest
62. stingy, sparing, miserly, mean, scanty
63. a list, set or system of names, terminology
64. lacking in warmth, enthusiasm or interest, indifferent
65. peerless, having no equal
66. severe home-sickness
67. quack remedy, patent medicine, pet scheme for reform
68. speculative, imaginary, pertaining to a notion
69. like a stepmother
70. a slight variation or shade of meaning, feeling etc.
71. trifling, worthless, invalid, futile
72. to annul, cancel, make void

A Language of Their Own

Most fields of human activity have a peculiar terminology, not always understood by the layman. Can you say in which sports, hobbies, professions or interests these groups of terms are used? You are *not* asked to give their meanings.

1. gules, argent, akimbo, rampant
2. option, placing, yield, bull
3. chinaman, gully, cover, yorker
4. foxing, impression, calf, marbled
5. spandrel, tympanum, clerestory, metope
6. occlusion, adiabatic, supercooled, isohyet
7. rallentando, sostenuto, diapason, breve
8. chert, Jurassic, porphyry, hornblende
9. catalyst, litmus, colloidal, precipitate
10. mashie, eagle, spoon, dormy
11. stadia, offset, resection, triangulation
12. perforated, mint, overprint, watermark
13. mulching, cloche, dibber, rust
14. reprise, flèche, coquille, tierce
15. focal length, rangefinder, cassette, condenser
16. binomial, quadratic, secant, mantissa
17. gouache, tempera, filbert, mahlstick
18. lynchet, fogou, cursus, megalith
19. face off, puck, penalty bench, alley
20. subliminal, schizoid, Rorschach, ambiversion
21. spinnaker, luff up, shrouds, pushpit
22. soubresaut, hortensia, épaulement, entrechat
23. macramé, picots, tatting, one passing
24. quatrain, hexameter, distich, anapaest

Answers on page 80

Something in Common

The words in each of the following groups are closely related or have something in common. Can you say what it is?

1. palladium, ytterbium, dysprosium, arsenic
2. bilharzia, beriberi, thrush, shingles
3. sackbut, serpent, ophicleide, rebec
4. saltarello, tarantella, seguidilla, schottische
5. cirrus, cumulus, stratus, nimbus
6. prolepsis, anacoluthon, zeugma, diaeresis
7. sombrero, fedora, kepi, fez
8. felucca, sampan, ketch, dhow
9. chinook, mistral, sirocco, khamsin
10. brougham, phaeton, landau, cabriolet
11. savannah, steppe, pampas, prairie
12. barbican, postern, bailey, portcullis
13. kale, kohlrabi, broccoli, artichoke
14. adze, awl, gimlet, plane
15. riesling, hock, sauternes, tokay
16. escritoire, davenport, whatnot, commode
17. vermouth, benedictine, chartreuse, absinth
18. melinite, lyddite, cordite, guncotton
19. coulomb, joule, henry, farad
20. gamboge, sienna, vermilion, indigo
21. lacrosse, fives, shinty, hurling
22. samoyed, borzoi, saluki, chihuahua
23. cuirass, pauldron, greave, gorget
24. cantilever, swing, bascule, transporter

Answers on page 80

There Must Be a Word For It!

Knowing the one and only word which exactly fits a given definition or meaning is a valuable asset. Can you give the words which fit these meanings?

1. The class of mammals which carry their young in a pouch.
2. Wreckage found floating on the surface of the sea.
3. The art of paper-folding.
4. A word or sentence that reads the same backwards and forwards.
5. Goods thrown overboard to lighten a ship.
6. A legendary animal with the head and wings of an eagle and the body of a lion.
7. An exaggerated statement not meant to be taken literally.
8. The rearing of silkworms for producing raw silk.
9. Fortune-telling by means of playing-cards.
10. Talking in one's sleep.
11. Living both on land and in water.
12. A two-hundredth anniversary
13. The collecting of postage-stamps.
14. The study of coins.
15. A small lizard which can change its colour.
16. A case for holding arrows.
17. A pair of eyeglasses with a spring which clips the nose.
18. A rain-water spout in the form of a grotesque human or animal head.
19. The killing of one's own brother.
20. The smallest pig of a litter.
21. A device intended to aid the memory.
22. The nesting-place of a swarm of bees.
23. A group of six persons or things.
24. The science of projectiles.

Col. 1. A Language of Their Own
Col. 2. Something in Common
Col. 3. There Must Be a Word For It!

1. Heraldry
2. Stockbroking
3. Cricket
4. Book collecting
5. Architecture
6. Meteorology
7. Music
8. Geology
9. Chemistry
10. Golf
11. Land surveying
12. Philately
13. Gardening
14. Fencing
15. Photography
16. Mathematics
17. Art
18. Archaeology
19. Ice Hockey
20. Psychology
21. Sailing
22. Ballet
23. Needlework
24. Poetry

1. Elements
2. Diseases
3. Old musical instruments
4. Dances
5. Clouds
6. Grammatical terms
7. Hats or head-gear
8. Boats
9. Winds
10. Carriages
11. Grassland plains
12. Parts of a castle
13. Vegetables
14. Tools
15. Wines
16. Furniture
17. Liqueurs
18. Explosives
19. Electrical units
20. Colours or pigments
21. Ball games
22. Dogs
23. Pieces of armour
24. Bridges

1. Marsupials
2. Flotsam
3. Origami
4. Palindrome
5. Jetsam
6. Griffin
7. Hyperbole
8. Sericulture
9. Cartomancy
10. Somniloquence
11. Amphibious
12. Bicentenary
13. Philately
14. Numismatics
15. Chameleon
16. Quiver
17. Pince-nez
18. Gargoyle
19. Fratricide
20. Tantony
21. Mnemonic
22. Honeycomb
23. Sextet
24. Ballistics

—'Ologies' and —'Meters'

Zoology is the science of the study of animals. To which branches of science or knowledge do these apply?

1. Algology	9. Gerontology	17. Ornithology
2. Barology	10. Graphology	18. Otology
3. Carpology	11. Herpetology	19. Philology
4. Cardiology	12. Hypnology	20. Palaeontology
5. Dendrology	13. Ichthyology	21. Rhinology
6. Entomology	14. Metrology	22. Speleology
7. Ethnology	15. Odontology	23. Toxicology
8. Etymology	16. Oology	24. Vulcanology

*   *   *

The suffix *-meter* is derived from the Latin *-metrum* — measure.
What do these instruments measure?

1. Altimeter	9. Echometer	17. Manometer
2. Ammeter	10. Galvanometer	18. Optometer
3. Anemometer	11. Goniometer	19. Opisometer
4. Bathometer	12. Hyetometer	20. Pedometer
5. Calorimeter	13. Hygrometer	21. Photometer
6. Chronometer	14. Lactometer	22. Pyrometer
7. Clinometer	15. Macrometer	23. Seismometer
8. Dasymeter	16. Micrometer	24. Tachometer

—'Ologies' and —'Meters'

1. Algae or seaweeds
2. Weight
3. Fruits
4. The heart
5. Trees
6. Insects
7. Races of mankind
8. Origin of words
9. Old age
10. Character from hand-writing
11. Reptiles
12. Sleep
13. Fishes
14. Weights and measures
15. Teeth
16. Birds' eggs
17. Birds
18. Ears and diseases of the ear
19. Language
20. Fossils
21. The nose
22. Caves
23. Poisons
24. Volcanoes

*   *   *

1. Altitude
2. Electric currents
3. Wind speed
4. Depth of water
5. Amount of heat or specific heat
6. Time
7. Slopes and altitudes
8. Density of gases
9. Duration of sounds
10. Electric (galvanic) currents
11. Angles
12. Rainfall
13. Humidity of air or gas
14. Specific gravity or purity of milk
15. Distant objects
16. Small objects, small distances
17. Elastic force of gases
18. Eyesight
19. Lines and distances on a map
20. Distance travelled on foot
21. Intensity of light
22. High temperatures
23. Earthquakes
24. Velocity of machines or of water

Complete the Word — L

Complete the following words from the given meanings.

1. Li . . id . . .   to wipe out, get rid of
2. L . n . . v . . .   long life
3. L . d . . r . . .   absurd, ridiculous
4. Le . . e . .   tolerant, gentle
5. Lo . t . . . m .   sickening, repulsive
6. L . . e . . c .   ability to read and write
7. Le . . t . t .   to make something rise in the air
8. L . . . l . u .   a type of floor-covering
9. L . s . . . u . e   weariness
10. L . . c . . . s   excessively sweet, cloying
11. Li . . i . .   a type of brown coal
12. L . . . n . . s   shining, bright, giving light
13. L . c . . t . . n .   growing in or relating to lakes
14. Lu . . a . . v .   gainful, profitable
15. L . t . . r . .   on or by the shore
16. L . . r . c . . e   to make smooth, apply oil or grease
17. L . . h .   supple, flexible
18. L . . . r . . e   to set free or release
19. L . u . . b . .   commendable, praiseworthy
20. L . . e . . c .   a nonsense verse of five lines
21. Lu . u . r . t . . .   nocturnal study or meditation
22. L . p . d . . .   a cutter or polisher of gems
23. L . . . nt . . . .   deplorable, regrettable
24. L . c . . . c   brief, concise

Answers on page 86

Complete the Word — M

Complete the following words from the given meanings.

1. M . d . . c . .   middling, indifferent
2. M . . d . m . . n . . .   an offence or misdeed
3. Mo . o . o . . .   a speech by, or scene for, one person
4. M . . . m . . p . . s .   to change the nature or form of
5. Mo . o . .   sullen, gloomy
6. M . . . . p   an unlucky accident
7. M . l . . . c . . . n   a curse
8. M . ll . . .   to appease or soften
9. M . . l . . . . m   a large whirlpool
10. M . . i . . p . l   of local government
11. M . l . . . h . l .   sadness, depression
12. M . r . . . t . .   type of inlaid work
13. M . . t . t . . e   a large gathering or crowd
14. M . . r . c . . .   representation in miniature, epitome
15. M . n . . . l . . .   to handle, manage with skill
16. Me . . t . r . . . s   deserving of reward or praise
17. M . . st . .   a large church or cathedral
18. M . n . . c . l .   very small (especially script)
19. M . n . . . n . . s   lacking variety
20. M . s . . c . .   slaughter, carnage
21. Ma . e . . a . i . e   to cause to appear, to make a fact
22. M . . z . . . n .   a low storey between two high ones
23. M . . d . . . n .   a beggar
24. M . u . o . e . .   a magnificent tomb

Answers on page 86

Complete the Word — N

Complete the following words from the given meanings.

1. N . g . l . . g   trifling, petty
2. No . o . . o . .   well-known, talked of
3. No . . . m .   harmful, objectionable
4. N . n . . s . . . p .   not easily described or classified
5. N . t . t .   to droop
6. N . t . . r . . . k   a species of toad
7. N . . r . g . .   a common gas
8. N . g . . c .   to omit to do, pay no attention to
9. N . . t l   of or by night
10. N . u . e . u .   offensive, nasty, disgusting
11. N . c . .   a recess in a wall
12. N . o . i . . . c   relating to the late Stone Age
13. N . c . . r . . e   a kind of peach
14. N . d . . .   a small rounded lump
15. Na . . . a . e   to sail, direct the course of
16. N . tr . . . n .   nourishing food
17. N . n . n . . . y   a non-existent thing, figment
18. N . . . l . . m   negative doctrines in religion
19. N . t . . k .   Japanese carved ornament
20. N . . o . . n .   a constituent of tobacco
21. N . . g . b . . rh . . .   nearness, vicinity of
22. N . . e . s . . .   indispensable, needful
23. N . r . . l . . . y   inclination to fall asleep
24. N . . . r   the lowest point of anything

Complete the Word

L	M	N
1. Liquidate	1. Mediocre	1. Niggling
2. Longevity	2. Misdemeanour	2. Notorious
3. Ludicrous	3. Monologue	3. Noisome
4. Lenient	4. Metamorphose	4. Nondescript
5. Loathsome	5. Morose	5. Nutate
6. Literacy	6. Mishap	6. Natterjack
7. Levitate	7. Malediction	7. Nitrogen
8. Linoleum	8. Mollify	8. Neglect
9. Lassitude	9. Maelstrom	9. Nocturnal
10. Luscious	10. Municipal	10. Nauseous
11. Lignite	11. Melancholy	11. Niche
12. Luminous	12. Marquetry	12. Neolithic
13. Lacustrine	13. Multitude	13. Nectarine
14. Lucrative	14. Microcosm	14. Nodule
15. Littoral	15. Manipulate	15. Navigate
16. Lubricate	16. Meritorious	16. Nutriment
17. Lithe	17. Minster	17. Nonentity
18. Liberate	18. Minuscule	18. Nihilism
19. Laudable	19. Monotonous	19. Netsuke
20. Limerick	20. Massacre	20. Nicotine
21. Lucubration	21. Materialize	21. Neighbourhood
22. Lapidary	22. Mezzanine	22. Necessary
23. Lamentable	23. Mendicant	23. Narcolepsy
24. Laconic	24. Mausoleum	24. Nadir

That's Odd!

There are some very odd words in the English language. Here are a few of them, some familiar and some not so familiar. How many do you know the meaning of?

1. Abracadabra
2. Alalia
3. Apoplexy
4. Balderdash
5. Bigwig
6. Blunderbuss
7. Blurb
8. Breastsummer
9. Calliope
10. Cantankerous
11. Circumbendi-bus
12. Collywobbles
13. Congeries
14. Coxcomb
15. Dumdum
16. Factotum
17. Feoffee
18. Fidibus
19. Fizgig
20. Flapdoodle
21. Flibberti-gibbet
22. Flim-flam
23. Galactagogue
24. Gazebo

25. Gewgaw
26. Ginkgo
27. Goatling
28. Grog-blossom
29. Hippophagy
30. Hobbledehoy
31. Hullabaloo
32. Ignicolist
33. Jackanapes
34. Jocoserious
35. Knicker-bockers
36. Lapis-lazuli
37. Loofah
38. Mangel-wurzel
39. Metagrobolize
40. Moiety
41. Molly-coddle
42. Mulligrubs
43. Mumbo Jumbo
44. Namby-pamby
45. Niminy-piminy
46. Nincompoop
47. Obloquy
48. Ogdoad

49. Pantechnicon
50. Peccadillo
51. Pettifogging
52. Picaroon
53. Poetaster
54. Quidnunc
55. Ragamuffin
56. Rapscallion
57. Rodomontade
58. Shemozzle
59. Shilly-shally
60. Slubberde-gullion
61. Spondee
62. Sprcad-eagle
63. Squeegee
64. Stickleback
65. Syzygy
66. Tatterdema-lion
67. Tittle-tattle
68. Topsy-turvy
69. Tussock
70. Vade-mecum
71. Wayzgoose
72. Weanling

That's Odd!

1. a spell, magic word or formula, gibberish
2. loss of speech
3. a malady which arrests the powers of sense and motion
4. a meaningless jumble of words
5. a man of high office or importance
6. a short gun with a large bore which fires many slugs
7. a publisher's advertisement for a book
8. a beam over a large opening, which holds up the super-structure
9. a musical instrument with steam-whistles and a keyboard
10. quarrelsome, cross-grained
11. a roundabout method, circumlocution
12. pain or rumbling in the intestines
13. a collection or mass of things heaped together
14. a foolish, conceited person
15. a type of bullet
16. a man of all-work, a servant who manages his master's affairs
17. a person to whom freehold estate is conveyed by feoffment
18. a paper spill for lighting a candle or pipe
19. a flighty woman, a kind of firework
20. nonsense talk
21. a gossip or flighty woman
22. nonsense, humbug, deception
23. anything which induces a flow of milk
24. a small building or room, usually in a garden, erected to obtain a view

That's Odd!

25. a gaudy toy or bauble, a showy trifle
26. a Japanese tree, also known as the maidenhair-tree
27. a goat over one year and under two years old
28. a redness of the nose caused by excessive drinking
29. the practice of eating horse-flesh
30. a clumsy or awkward youth between boyhood and manhood
31. a tumultuous noise, uproar
32. a fire-worshipper
33. an upstart or impertinent fellow
34. half jocular, half serious
35. type of loose-fitting breeches
36. a bright blue silicate and pigment
37. a sponge or brush made of plant-fibre
38. a vegetable, a variety of beet
39. to puzzle or mystify, to puzzle out
40. a half, one of two parts
41. to coddle a person; one who is coddled or nursed
42. a state of depression, stomach-ache
43. an object of senseless veneration
44. feebly sentimental, insipidly pretty
45. mincing, affected, lacking in spirit
46. a fool, blockhead or simpleton
47. abuse, detraction, evil-speaking, being ill-spoken of
48. the number eight, or a set or group of eight

That's Odd!

49. a furniture warehouse, a furniture-removing van
50. a trifling offence or fault
51. chicanery, petty quibbling
52. a rogue, thief, pirate
53. a paltry poet
54. an inquisitive person, gossip, newsmonger
55. a ragged, dirty fellow
56. a rascal, rogue, vagabond
57. boastful talk, extravagant bragging
58. a quarrel, muddle or mêlée
59. to vacillate, be irresolute or undecided
60. a slobbering or dirty fellow
61. a metrical foot of two long syllables
62. to fasten or stretch out like a spread eagle, to beat completely
63. a long-handled implement for removing water
64. a small fish
65. conjunction or opposition (in astronomy)
66. a ragged or beggarly fellow
67. chatter, prattle, gossip
68. upside down, disorderly
69. a tuft or clump of grass
70. a book or thing carried about on the person
71. printers' annual outing or festivity
72. a newly-weaned child or animal

What's Wrong Here?

It is all too easy to make mistakes in grammar; even the best writers slip up occasionally. Here are some sentences for you to correct; each contains at least one simple error.

1. The value of the contents of the house were more than I thought.
2. On Friday neither the train or the coach were on time.
3. The money was divided between my brother, my sister, and myself.
4. He is the cleverest of all the others in his class.
5. Having been stolen, the Bank refused to cash his cheque.
6. There will be trouble if either of these pictures are lost.
7. It was me who wrote that letter.
8. It is not really necessary to do like I do.
9. None of the trains this morning have been on time.
10. We only saw it the other day.
11. This is the opposite to the one you have.
12. He lost his wallet between the river or the canal.
13. By filling in this form, ten pounds may be won.
14. This is one of the best books on chess which has ever been written.
15. That is the person whom we think sent the letter.
16. There will be an interval between each scene.
17. The vote, with two exceptions, was unanimously against it.
18. Each of us is much too concerned with our own base desires.
19. He has a Mercedes and an Austin; the former is easily the fastest.
20. There were a number of boys there already.
21. Unlike most children's books, these characters were rather grim.
22. Eventually he had to agree with my proposals.
23. The eight boys understood each other well enough.
24. After defending grimly for ten minutes, the ball was kicked upfield.

What's Wrong Here?

1. The value of the contents of the house *was* more than I thought.
2. On Friday neither the train *nor* the coach *was* on time.
3. The money was divided *among* my brother, my sister, and myself.
4. He is the cleverest of all in his class.
5. Having been stolen, his cheque was refused at the Bank.
6. There will be trouble if either of these pictures *is* lost.
7. It was *I* who wrote that letter.
8. It is not really necessary to do *as* I do.
9. None of the trains this morning *has* been on time.
10. We saw it only the other day.
11. This is the opposite *of* the one you have.
12. He lost his wallet between the river *and* the canal.
13. By filling in this form, one may win ten pounds.
14. This is one of the best books on chess which *have* ever been written.
15. That is the person *who* we think sent the letter.
16. There will be an interval between each scene and the next one.
17. All except two of the votes were against it.
18. Each of us is much too concerned with *his or her* own base desires.
19. He has a Mercedes and an Austin; the former is easily the *faster*.
20. There *was* a number of boys there already.
21. Unlike the characters in most children's books, these were rather grim.
22. Eventually he had to agree *to* my proposals.
23. The eight boys understood *one another* well enough.
24. After defending grimly for ten minutes, they kicked the ball upfield.

What Does This Word Mean?
No. 5

Give the meanings of these words.

1. Obdurate
2. Obliterate
3. Oboe
4. Obsequious
5. Obstreperous
6. Ochlocracy
7. Officious
8. Oleaginous
9. Opaque
10. Opine
11. Opprobrium
12. Opulent
13. Orchestrate
14. Orifice
15. Ormolu
16. Orotund
17. Ossify
18. Ostensible
19. Ostentation
20. Ostracize
21. Otiose
22. Ovation
23. Overt
24. Ovoid

25. Palatable
26. Palpable
27. Paradigm
28. Parsimonious
29. Pellucid
30. Penurious
31. Peremptory
32. Perfunctory
33. Perspicacious
34. Pertinacious
35. Phrenetic
36. Pliable
37. Ponderous
38. Pragmatism
39. Precocious
40. Predilection
41. Premeditated
42. Presentiment
43. Prestidigitation
44. Prevaricate
45. Procrastinate
46. Promulgate
47. Punctilious
48. Pusillanimous

49. Ramify
50. Rancour
51. Rapacious
52. Ratiocinate
53. Recalcitrant
54. Recollect
55. Recondite
56. Recrudesce
57. Redolent
58. Refulgent
59. Remonstrate
60. Reprehend
61. Rescind
62. Resuscitate
63. Reticulate
64. Rhabdomancy
65. Rigmarole
66. Risible
67. Rococo
68. Rotund
69. Rubicund
70. Rubiginous
71. Rumbustious
72. Ruse

What Does This Word Mean?
No. 5

1. hardened in evil, unyielding, stubborn
2. to erase, efface, blot out, delete
3. a musical instrument
4. servile, fawning, sycophantic
5. noisy, vociferous, unruly
6. government by mob-rule
7. doing more than required, meddlesome
8. having properties of oil, producing oil, oily, greasy
9. not transmitting light, not transparent, obscure
10. to hold or express an opinion
11. disgrace, infamy, reproach
12. rich, wealthy
13. to compose or arrange for an orchestra
14. an aperture, vent, or perforation
15. gilded bronze, gold-coloured alloy of copper, zinc and tin
16. imposing or dignified way of speaking, inflated, pompous
17. to turn into bone, to harden
18. professed, pretended, put forth as genuine
19. pretentious display, showing-off
20. to banish, expel, exclude from society etc.
21. superfluous, useless, sterile
22. enthusiastic applause
23. open to view, evident, unconcealed
24. like an egg, egg-shaped

What Does This Word Mean? No. 5

25. pleasant to the taste, savoury
26. tangible, readily perceived, apparent, obvious
27. an example, pattern
28. careful with money, sparing
29. transparent, clear
30. poor, needy, grudging
31. dogmatic, imperious, intolerant, dictatorial
32. done as routine or without interest, superficial
33. having mental penetration or discernment
34. persistent, stubborn, obstinate
35. frantic, fanatic
36. flexible, supple, yielding
37. heavy, massive, unwieldy, laborious
38. pedantry, matter-of-fact treatment, a philosophical doctrine
39. prematurely developed, fruiting early
40. a mental preference, partiality
41. previously planned, thought out beforehand
42. foreboding, vague expectation
43. sleight of hand, conjuring
44. to speak or act evasively, equivocate
45. to defer, delay
46. to make known, proclaim
47. attentive to or observant of nice points of behaviour
48. faint-hearted, cowardly, mean-spirited

What Does This Word Mean?
No. 5

49. to form branches, branch out, spread like branches
50. bitter ill-feeling, malignant hatred, spitefulness
51. grasping, greedy, predatory
52. to reason
53. disobedient, refractory
54. to recall to mind, remember
55. abstruse, obscure, profound
56. to break out again
57. smelling of, full of the smell or scent of
58. shining brilliantly, radiant
59. to protest against, expostulate
60. to rebuke, censure, find fault with
61. to annul, revoke, repeal
62. to restore to life or revive
63. to divide or be divided into a network
64. divining by use of a rod, especially for water
65. rambling or meaningless talk, incoherent
66. inclined to laughter, relating to laughter
67. a highly-ornate style of eighteenth-century art
68. (of speech) sonorous, (of persons) rounded, plump
69. ruddy, reddish, red-faced
70. rusty, rust-coloured
71. boisterous, uproarious
72. a trick or stratagem

What's the Trouble?

A *phobia* is a fear or dread of some particular thing. To what do these phobias apply?

1. Agoraphobia
2. Bathophobia
3. Claustrophobia
4. Cynophobia
5. Ergophobia
6. Gynophobia
7. Nyctophobia
8. Phobophobia
9. Phonophobia
10. Scopophobia
11. Xenophobia
12. Zoophobia

*　　*　　*

A *mania* is a compulsive desire or craze for something. Can you say what things are desired by people with these manias?

1. Agromania
2. Bibliomania
3. Chirablutomania
4. Chronomania
5. Dipsomania
6. Dromomania
7. Kleptomania
8. Megalomania
9. Metromania
10. Nostomania
11. Pyromania
12. Sophomania

*　　*　　*

The following are all diseases or ailments of the body. Do you know which part of the body they each affect?

1. Arthritis
2. Bronchitis
3. Colitis
4. Conjunctivitis
5. Dermatitis
6. Gastritis
7. Hepatitis
8. Meningitis
9. Neuritis
10. Phlebitis
11. Poliomyelitis
12. Stomatitis

What's the Trouble?

Phobias:

1. open or public places
2. falling from a height
3. enclosed spaces
4. dogs
5. being active
6. women
7. darkness or night
8. being afraid
9. certain sounds
10. being stared at
11. strangers
12. animals

* * *

Manias:

1. to be alone
2. to collect books
3. excessive handwashing
4. perfectionism in timekeeping
5. alcohol
6. to wander
7. to steal
8. to have great power
9. to compose verse
10. longing for home
11. to start fires
12. belief in one's own wisdom

* * *

-Itises:

1. joints
2. lungs
3. colon or intestines
4. eye
5. skin
6. stomach
7. liver
8. brain and spinal cord
9. nerves
10. veins
11. spinal cord
12. mouth

The Long and the Short of It

Here are some extra-long words, some very short words, and a collection of odd words beginning with 'H'. You may not know many of the long words, but you should know most of the short ones.

1. Ambidextrous
2. Brachycephalic
3. Canaliculate
4. Commiseration
5. Condominium
6. Equiponderant
7. Flocci-nauci-nihili-pili-fication
8. Fore-topgallant
9. Funambulist
10. Impalpability
11. Indefatigable
12. Isoperimetrical
13. Lepidopterist
14. Malacoderma-tous
15. Octingentenary
16. Parallelepiped
17. Premonstraten-sian
18. Reverberation
19. Sanguification
20. Sesquipedalian
21. Tergiversation
22. Testudinarious
23. Ultracrepidarian
24. Valetudinarian

25. Acrid
26. Aft
27. Aloof
28. Banal
29. Crypt
30. Doggo
31. Eke
32. Fez
33. Flair
34. Fop
35. Glut
36. Haply
37. Ingot
38. Mete
39. Muggy
40. Numb
41. Opal
42. Pawky
43. Rabid
44. Rant
45. Salvo
46. Tryst
47. Vapid
48. Vial

49. Hab-nab
50. Handy-dandy
51. Hanky-panky
52. Harum-scarum
53. Heebie-jeebies
54. Helter-skelter
55. Hiccius doccius
56. Higgledy-piggledy
57. Hitty-missy
58. Hob-nob
59. Hocus-pocus
60. Hoddy-doddy
61. Hogen Mogen
62. Hoi polloi
63. Hoity-toity
64. Holus-bolus
65. Hotchpotch
66. Hot-pot
67. Hubble-bubble
68. Hugger-mugger
69. Humdrum
70. Humpty-dumpty
71. Hurdy-gurdy
72. Hurly-burly

The Long and the Short of It

1. being able to use both hands equally well
2. short-headed, short-skulled
3. having a longitudinal groove or minute channel
4. pity or sorrow for another person's distress
5. joint control of a state's affairs by other states
6. of equal weight, evenly balanced
7. the action of estimating as worthless
8. the mast above the fore-topmast of a ship
9. a rope-walker or rope-dancer
10. the quality of being imperceptible to the touch or intangible
11. incapable of being tired out or wearied, unremitting
12. having equal perimeters
13. a person who studies butterflies and moths
14. having a soft skin (of animals)
15. the eight-hundredth anniversary of an event
16. a solid figure contained by six parallelograms
17. an order of regular canons
18. the return or re-echoing of sounds or light
19. the formation of blood, conversion into blood
20. a word of many syllables, given to long words
21. the forsaking or deserting of a cause or party
22. of the character of a tortoise
23. going beyond one's province or knowledge
24. a person in poor health, especially one concerned with his own ailments

The Long and the Short of It

25. bitter, pungent, corrosive, irritating
26. near or towards the stern
27. at a distance from, apart
28. commonplace, trite, trivial
29. an underground chamber or vault, especially beneath a church
30. to lie quiet or hidden
31. to increase, add to, supplement
32. a Turkish skull-cap in the form of a cone
33. discernment, instinct for what is excellent
34. a dandy, a vain man
35. a surfeit of a commodity; to feed or fill to excess
36. by chance or accident; perhaps
37. a mass of cast metal, especially of gold, silver or steel
38. to measure, deal out, allot
39. damp, close and warm, stifling
40. deprived of feeling, helpless
41. a type of gemstone
42. artful, sly, cunning, shrewd
43. furious, violent, unreasoning
44. to speak bombastically or loudly; empty talk or tirade
45. a salute by artillery guns; a reservation or saving clause
46. an agreement to meet at a certain place and time
47. flat, dull, insipid, lifeless
48. a small vessel for holding liquids

The Long and the Short of It

49. get or lose, hit or miss, anyhow
50. a children's game in which an object is concealed in the hand
51. jugglery, trickery, double dealing
52. reckless, wild, rash
53. a dance resembling the blues, also the blues
54. in disorderly haste; pell-mell; a large slide in a fairground
55. magic words or formula used by jugglers
56. confusion or disorderly jumble
57. hit or miss, random, haphazard
58. to drink together, be on familiar terms with
59. jugglery, trickery, deception
60. short and dumpy, a snail (dialect)
61. a contemptuous word for the Dutch (formerly the high and mighty)
62. the masses, the rabble
63. frolicsome, petulant, flighty
64. all in a hump, all at once
65. a mixture, medley, jumble
66. a dish of meat and potatoes cooked in a pot
67. a type of Eastern smoking-pipe; also confused talk
68. disorderly, confused; also secret, clandestine
69. commonplace, monotonous, dull
70. a short, dumpy person
71. a musical instrument played by turning a handle; also name given to the barrel-organ
72. commotion, uproar, confusion

Complete the Word — O

Complete the following words from the given meanings:

1. O . . . . . s   a type of vehicle
2. O . . r . . s   burdensome
3. O . . . c . . n   a maker of spectacles
4. O . . o . . n   a type of seat
5. O . l . . . t . . y   legally or morally binding
6. O . . r . g . . . s   immoderate, extravagant
7. O . r . r .   a model of the planetary system
8. O . . . l . . t .   to swing like a pendulum, vacillate
9. O . n . x . o . .   offensive, objectionable
10. O . u . . . t   an eye-specialist
11. O . . l . s .   a tall stone monument
12. O . . n . . s   inauspicious, threatening
13. O . v . . t .   to get round, prevent
14. O . . or . . n .   favourable, well-timed
15. O . s . . . t .   disused, antiquated
16. O . n . . e   elaborately decorated or adorned
17. Ob . i . i . . .   forgetful, unmindful of
18. O . t . m . .   the best or most favourable
19. O . t . . d . .   conventional, correct
20. O . . . . n   a gas essential to life
21. O . c . . r . . c .   a happening or incident
22. O . . . . e . a . . . n   a person eighty years old
23. O . t . . e   blunt, dull, stupid
24. O . st . c . .   a hindrance or impediment

Answers on page 106

Complete the Word — P

Complete the following words from the given meanings:

1. P . . d . . . m . . t an unpleasant or dangerous situation
2. P . . v . . . n . having foresight, thrifty
3. P . . n . c . . . s quarrelsome, given to fighting
4. P . o . . r . . e lying face downwards on the ground
5. P . r . . c . . . s destructive, ruinous
6. P . . s . g . to portend, give warning of
7. P . t . l . . t peevishly impatient, irritable
8. P . . t . t . . . a commonplace remark
9. P . . d . . . l wasteful, lavish
10. P . . d . . o . . u . uproar, confusion
11. P . o . . f . . abundantly productive of
12. P . . t . . . t . . . type of leather trunk
13. P . n . . . n . repentant, contrite
14. P . r . . r . t . to make holes in, pierce
15. P . . m . . . . t supreme, pre-eminent
16. P . . p . . t . . o . . absurd, ridiculous
17. P . t . . t . t . a monarch or ruler
18. P . . g . . n . sharp, pungent
19. P . r . x . s . a fit of rage or laughter
20. Pr . . . nt . . . s ostentatious, claiming great merit
21. P . . . p . . . y boundary line or surface
22. P . u . . . t discreet, judicious
23. P . . m . n . . . connected with the lungs
24. P . . . . d decomposed, rotten

Answers on page 106

Complete the Word — R

Complete the following words from the given meanings.

1. Re . . m . . . t   lying down, reclining
2. R . . . c . . e   the killing of a king
3. R . p . r . . e   a witty reply or retort
4. R . m . . e . . t .   to reward or pay for services
5. R . . r . m . n .   to rebuke, reprove, censure
6. R . . l . . a   a duplicate or facsimile
7. R . . s . . c . l .   rickety, tumble-down
8. R . s . n . . t   re-echoing, resounding
9. R . tr . . . o . r   part of a cathedral or church
10. R . f . . c . . . y   stubborn, rebellious
11. R . s . . u .   remainder, rest
12. R . s . l . . d . . t   shining, brilliant
13. R . u . . us   hoarse, harsh-sounding
14. R . . t . . m   a platform for public speakers
15. R . . i . . l . . .   absurd, laughable
16. R . d . . d . n .   superfluous, excessive
17. R . . d . d . . d . . .   a type of evergreen shrub
18. R . s . . . t .   determined, unshrinking
19. R . c . p . . c . .   inversely correspondent, complement-ary
20. R . v . r . . r . . .   to re-echo, reflect, return
21. R . v . . o . .   famished, hungry
22. R . . . l . . . n   armed resistance, revolt
23. R . . . v . . . t .   to make young again
24. R . c . p . . . t .   to restore, recover from illness

Complete the Word

O	P	R
1. Omnibus	1. Predicament	1. Recumbent
2. Onerous	2. Provident	2. Regicide
3. Optician	3. Pugnacious	3. Repartee
4. Ottoman	4. Prostrate	4. Remunerate
5. Obligatory	5. Pernicious	5. Reprimand
6. Outrageous	6. Presage	6. Replica
7. Orrery	7. Petulant	7. Ramshackle
8. Oscillate	8. Platitude	8. Resonant
9. Obnoxious	9. Prodigal	9. Retrochoir
10. Oculist	10. Pandemonium	10. Refractory
11. Obelisk	11. Prolific	11. Residue
12. Ominous	12. Portmanteau	12. Resplendent
13. Obviate	13. Penitent	13. Raucous
14. Opportune	14. Perforate	14. Rostrum
15. Obsolete	15. Prominent	15. Ridiculous
16. Ornate	16. Preposterous	16. Redundant
17. Oblivious	17. Potentate	17. Rhododendron
18. Optimum	18. Poignant	18. Resolute
19. Orthodox	19. Paroxysm	19. Reciprocal
20. Oxygen	20. Pretentious	20. Reverberate
21. Occurrence	21. Periphery	21. Ravenous
22. Octogenarian	22. Prudent	22. Rebellion
23. Obtuse	23. Pulmonary	23. Rejuvenate
24. Obstacle	24. Putrid	24. Recuperate

Malapropisms

Mrs. Malaprop, a character in Sheridan's play *The Rivals*, had a habit of misusing words by confusing them with similar words. Hence this practice, or an instance of it, has become known as a *malapropism*. The following passage contains some malapropisms for you to correct.

The train pulled into the station. I looked in all the carriages, but could not decry the person I sought. I took the unsigned letter from my pocket again; I knew who had written this anomalous letter to me – John Smith. 'Will arrive on the 3.15 train', it read. But there was no sign of the illusive Smith and the departure of the train was eminent. The fact that he had not arrived effected me strangely. How could anybody so fragrantly break their promise? As I walked away I almost evinced myself that the whole incidence was imaginative, and that I had temporally taken leave of my senses.

Then a man accosted me. 'Excuse me, sir', he said respectably, 'but I have a message for you. Mr. Smith thinks it desirous that you should not take any precipitous action over the train incident, which might mitigate against further good relations'. I thought quickly. 'I'm not adverse to forgetting the incident', I said judicially, 'but the principal of the thing is what matters'. 'Don't put a literate interpolation on that note', he said. 'You have put me in an insidious position', I replied. 'You are trying to tell me that Mr. Smith is innocuous of any intention to mislead me, but I know very well that he is quite capacious of doing that very thing'.

Malapropisms

This is how the passage should read.

The train pulled into the station. I looked in all the carriages, but could not *descry* the person I sought. I took the unsigned letter from my pocket again; I knew who had written this *anonymous* letter to me – John Smith. 'Will arrive on the 3.15 train', it read. But there was no sign of the *elusive* Smith and the departure of the train was *imminent*. The fact that he had not arrived *affected* me strangely. How could anybody so *flagrantly* break their promise? As I walked away I almost *convinced* myself that the whole *incident* was *imaginary*, and that I had *temporarily* taken leave of my senses.

Then a man accosted me. 'Excuse me, sir', he said *respectfully*, 'but I have a message for you. Mr. Smith thinks it *desirable* that you should not take any *precipitate* action over the train incident, which might *militate* against further good relations'. I thought quickly. 'I'm not *averse* to forgetting the incident', I said *judiciously*, 'but the *principle* of the thing is what matters'. 'Don't put a *literal interpretation* on that note', he said. 'You have put me in an *invidious* position', I replied. 'You are trying to tell me that Mr. Smith is *innocent* of any intention to mislead me, but I know very well that he is quite *capable* of doing that very thing'.

Not Quite the Same!

There are many words that are often confused with other somewhat similar words. Can you explain the difference between the two words in each pair?

1.	Continual	and	continuous
2.	Alternate		alternative
3.	Practical		practicable
4.	Decompose		discompose
5.	Cryptogam		cryptogram
6.	Gourmand		gourmet
7.	Deprecate		depreciate
8.	Exceptional		exceptionable
9.	Luxuriant		luxurious
10.	Mendacity		mendicity
11.	Desiccate		desecrate
12.	Elicit		illicit
13.	Titillate		titivate
14.	Turbid		turgid
15.	Venal		venial
16.	Inflammable		inflammatory
17.	Tractable		tractile
18.	Ingenious		ingenuous
19.	Abrogate		arrogate
20.	Adhere		cohere
21.	Credible		creditable
22.	Equable		equitable
23.	Contemptible		contemptuous
24.	Deduce		deduct

Not Quite the Same!

1. Continual = always going on, perpetual, incessant, never coming to an end. Continuous = unbroken from start to finish, uninterrupted in time or sequence.
2. Alternate = by turns, i.e. two things succeeding each other in turn, one after the other. Alternative = the choice of one of two things or courses of action.
3. Practical = of or relating to the practice of something as opposed to the theory. Practicable = capable of being carried out or accomplished, feasible.
4. Decompose = to separate into constituent parts or elements, to decay or rot. Discompose = to disturb the composure or calmness of, to agitate or ruffle.
5. Cryptogam = a species of plant with no stamens and pistils and no flowers. Cryptogram = something in cypher or code.
6. Gourmand = a judge or lover of good eating. Gourmet = a connoisseur of good food, delicacies and wine.
7. Deprecate = to plead or pray against something, to express disapproval of. Depreciate = to diminish in value, to disparage or belittle.
8. Exceptional = forming an exception, out of the ordinary, unusual. Exceptionable = open to exception or objection.
9. Luxuriant = growing profusely, exuberant, prolific, rich, producing abundantly. Luxurious = given to luxury or self-indulgence.

Not Quite the Same!

10. Mendacity = untruthfulness, habitual lying or deceiving. Mendicity = the practice of begging, the condition of a beggar.
11. Desiccate = to make dry, or dry up for preservation. Desecrate = to commit outrage on or profane something sacred.
12. Elicit = to draw forth, to draw out information, to evoke a response. Illicit = unlawful, forbidden, not allowed by law, rule or custom.
13. Titillate = to excite or stimulate the mind or senses, to tickle. Titivate = to make oneself more attractive by small additions to one's toilet, to put the finishing touches to something.
14. Turbid = not clear, cloudy, muddy, mentally confused or muddled. Turgid = swollen, distended, inflated.
15. Venal — of persons capable of being bought over, of a mercenary character, of offices etc. capable of being acquired by purchase. Venial = not grave, trivial, worthy of pardon or forgiveness.
16. Inflammable = capable of being inflamed, easily set on fire (strangely enough 'flammable' means exactly the same). Inflammatory = tending to excite passion or anger, to inflame the blood, to stimulate.
17. Tractable = easily managed, docile, compliant. Tractile — that which can be drawn, e.g. money from a bank.

Not Quite the Same!

18. Ingenious = showing cleverness of invention or construction. Ingenuous = straightforward, open, candid, frank, artless.
19. Abrogate = to repeal or do away with. Arrogate = to claim that which one is not entitled to, to appropriate without reason, to assume without foundation.
20. Adhere = to stick fast to something, to cleave to a person or party. Cohere = to stick together, to be united in action.
21. Credible = capable of being believed. Creditable = that which brings credit or honour, reputable.
22. Equable = uniform, free from inequalities or variation. Equitable = characterized by fairness and impartiality.
23. Contemptible = worthy of contempt, despicable. Contemptuous = showing contempt, disdainful, scornful.
24. Deduce = to draw as a conclusion from something known or assumed, to derive by reasoning, to infer. Deduct = to take away or subtract from a sum or amount.

What Does This Word Mean?
No. 6

Give the meanings of these words.

1. Salubrious
2. Sarcophagus
3. Scintillate
4. Scurrilous
5. Sedulous
6. Senescent
7. Sententious
8. Serendipity
9. Sibilant
10. Sumulacrum
11. Smithereens
12. Solicitous
13. Somnolent
14. Sonorous
15. Soupçon
16. Specious
17. Sporadic
18. Stratagem
19. Strident
20. Suave
21. Sullen
22. Sultry
23. Sumptuous
24. Surreptitious

25. Taciturn
26. Talisman
27. Tarantella
28. Tarantula
29. Tawdry
30. Temerity
31. Tendentious
32. Tenuous
33. Thaumaturge
34. Thrall
35. Timorous
36. Tintinnabu-
    lation
37. Torpid
38. Tortuous
39. Toxophily
40. Traduce
41. Transmute
42. Tremulous
43. Trenchant
44. Tribulation
45. Truculent
46. Tumid
47. Tutelage
48. Typography

49. Ubiquitous
50. Umbrage
51. Unkempt
52. Uxorious
53. Vacillate
54. Vacuous
55. Vehement
56. Verbatim
57. Verisimilitude
58. Vermicular
59. Vespiary
60. Vicarage
61. Vicinity
62. Virile
63. Virulent
64. Viscous
65. Vituperate
66. Volatile
67. Voracious
68. Vouchsafe
69. Waive
70. Whimsical
71. Whittle
72. Wreckage

What Does This Word Mean?
No. 6

1. favourable to health, healthy
2. a stone coffin
3. to sparkle, twinkle, emit sparks
4. coarseness of language, grossly abusive
5. diligent, persistent, assiduous
6. growing old, elderly
7. aphoristic, affectedly formal, given to moralizing
8. the knack of making happy discoveries by accident
9. having or making a hissing sound
10. an image, imitation or likeness of something
11. small fragments
12. anxious, eager, troubled, concerned
13. sleepy, drowsy
14. loud-sounding, resonant, having a full voice
15. a very small quantity or dash of something
16. apparently attractive or plausible but not genuine or sincere
17. occurring here and there, scattered, isolated
18. an artifice or trick
19. loud and harsh, shrill
20. pleasing, agreeable, soothing, blandly polite
21. ill-humoured, morose, unsociable, dismal
22. oppressively hot
23. costly and magnificent
24. secret, clandestine, stealthy

What Does This Word Mean?
No. 6

25. reserved in speech, not given to talking
26. a charm, amulet
27. a South Italian dance
28. a large spider
29. cheap finery, showy but worthless
30. rashness, recklessness
31. having an underlying purpose, or a purposed tendency
32. thin, slender, unsubstantial
33. a worker of miracles, wonder-worker
34. a serf or slave, bondage, servitude, enslaved
35. timid, full of fear
36. bell-ringing, the tinkling of bells
37. numb, dormant, sluggish, apathetic
38. full of twists, winding, crooked, devious
39. the practice of archery
40. to misrepresent, defame, slander
41. to change the form or nature of, convert, alter
42. trembling, quivering, fearful
43. incisive, clear-cut, decisive
44. severe suffering or affliction, oppression
45. fierce, cruel, ferocious, scathing, savage
46. swollen, inflated, protuberant
47. guardianship, tuition, under protection
48. the art of printing, the arrangement of printed matter

What Does This Word Mean? No. 6

49. everywhere present, widely distributed
50. resentment, offence, sense of slight
51. untidy, of neglected appearance
52. excessively devoted to one's wife
53. to waver, oscillate, sway from side to side
54. empty, void, expressionless
55. violent, intense, ardent, with great force or strength
56. word for word
57. the appearance or semblance of being true
58. worm-like, wavy
59. a wasps' nest
60. the benefice or residence of a vicar
61. nearness to, surrounding district
62. manly, full of masculine strength
63. poisonous, malignant
64. like glue, sticky, not fluid
65. to abuse, revile
66. changeable, transient, readily vanishing or evaporating
67. greedy, ravenous
68. condescend to do or give something
69. to forgo or relinquish a right or claim
70. capricious, fantastic, full of whims
71. to slice or shave with a knife, to wear away or reduce
72. remnants of a wrecked vessel, house etc.

It's the Same Word!

There are many words which, though spelt the same, have two or more quite different meanings; they are known as *homonyms*. Can you supply the word which fits these meanings?

1. to find fault; a species of fish
2. a species of tree; a carpenter's tool
3. a small sum or amount; a sweet confection
4. a mail-boat; a small parcel
5. a species of mammal; a stamp or impression of authenticity
6. a period of the year; to mature or ripen
7. the capital funds of a company; a flower
8. a receptacle; a species of tree
9. relating to the body; a military rank
10. a forest-tree; the residue of burning
11. a current of air; a preliminary sketch or plan
12. a recurring verse in song; to abstain or forbear
13. a garment; a headland
14. a sharp reply; a vessel for heating liquids
15. part of a ship; a card-game
16. a large bird; a machine for raising things
17. useless odds-and-ends; to move heavily
18. a narrow pass; to corrupt or befoul
19. a species of fish; a deep voice or sound
20. kind of beer; a gate-keeper
21. an obsolete weapon; a species of fish
22. a tiresome talkative person; a tidal-wave
23. a tool; a military exercise
24. a measure; a fish's organ

Answers on page 120

—'isms'

The words which fit the following meanings all end in '–*ism*'. How many do you know?

1. A new word or expression, or the use of new words.
2. A ridiculous misuse of a word, usually for one resembling it.
3. The transposition of the beginnings of two adjacent words.
4. The use of another person's thoughts or writings as one's own.
5. A mild expression used as a substitute for a blunt one.
6. Artificial or affected style of writing.
7. The art style which presents objects as geometrical shapes.
8. Denial of the existence of a God.
9. Belief that the existence of God cannot be known or proved.
10. Doctrine that all is God and God is all.
11. Belief in God without proof or revelation.
12. Sleep-walking.
13. Perversion in which sufferer derives pleasure from pain.
14. Belief that everything that happens is predetermined by fate.
15. An expression belonging to ordinary conversation or common speech.
16. A principle expressed concisely, a maxim.
17. Conduct expressing patient endurance and repression of feelings.
18. The action of passing judgement upon anything; fault-finding.
19. Artificially producing a state of deep sleep.
20. Religious rite of initiation into the Church.
21. Regard for others as a principle of action.
22. Exaggerated and warlike patriotism
23. An old or obsolete word or expression.
24. Art form which represents the phenomena of dreams and the subconscious.

The Missing Word

Give the missing word from each of these famous quotations.

1. Water, water, everywhere. Nor * drop to drink.
2. For fools rush in where angels fear to * .
3. * is the last refuge of a scoundrel.
4. There is no sin except * .
5. Never in the field of human * was so much owed by so many to so few.
6. The curfew tolls the * of parting day.
7. And what * they know of England who only England know.
8. Government of the people, by the people, and * the people . . .
9. Friends, Romans, countrymen, * me your ears . . .
10. Once more unto the breach, dear * ,once more;
11. The * of a thing well done, is to have done it.
12. Reading maketh a full man, conference a ready man, and writing an * man.
13. 'Will you walk a little faster?', said a * to a snail.
14. 'It's as large as life, and twice as * .'
15. Let not poor * starve.
16. If * did not exist it would be necessary to invent him.
17. Which of you by taking thought can add one cubit unto his *
18. A prophet is not without honour, * in his own country.
19. O Death, where is thy sting? O * , where is thy victory?
20. Though patience be a tired * , yet she will plod.
21. Now is the winter of our discontent made * summer by the sun of York.
22. In Xanadu did Kubla Khan a stately * decree.
23. To * is human, to forgive, divine.
24. No man but a * ever wrote except for money.

119

Column 1 — It's the Same Word
Column 2 — —'isms'
Column 3 — The Missing Word

1. Carp	1. Neologism	1. Any
2. Plane	2. Malapropism	2. Tread
3. Trifle	3. Spoonerism	3. Patriotism
4. Packet	4. Plagiarism	4. Stupidity
5. Seal	5. Euphemism	5. Conflict
6. Season	6. Euphuism	6. Knell
7. Stock	7. Cubism	7. Should
8. Box	8. Atheism	8. For
9. Corporal	9. Agnosticism	9. Lend
10. Ash	10. Pantheism	10. Friends
11. Draught	11. Deism	11. Reward
12. Refrain	12. Somnambulism	12. Exact
13. Cape	13. Masochism	13. Whiting
14. Retort	14. Fatalism	14. Natural
15. Bridge	15. Colloquialism	15. Nelly
16. Crane	16. Aphorism	16. God
17. Lumber	17. Stoicism	17. Stature
18. Defile	18. Criticism	18. Save
19. Bass	19. Hypnotism	19. Grave
20. Porter	20. Baptism	20. Mare
21. Pike	21. Altruism	21. Glorious
22. Bore	22. Chauvinism	22. Pleasure-dome
23. Drill	23. Archaism	23. Err
24. Gill	24. Surrealism	24. Blockhead

Complete the Word — S

Complete the following words from the given meanings.

1. Se ... h . . e   a type of signalling apparatus
2. S . . g . . s .   inactive, torpid, indolent
3. S . p . . . f . .   tending to produce sleep
4. S . n . . s . .   a summary or conspectus
5. S . n . . . s   tortuous, undulating
6. S . . . l . . r . l   funereal, dismal
7. S . c . . h . . t   a flatterer or toady
8. S . . d . n . .   bitter, scornful, cynical
9. S . b . . . t   to disturb or overthrow
10. S . r . . . . d   having a saw-like edge
11. S . g . . g . . .   to set apart, separate
12. S . . . c . . . n .   a deadly poison
13. S . . m . . .   power of resistance or endurance
14. S . c . . s . . c .   inviolable, sacred
15. So . . c . . m   a grammatical error
16. S . r . n . . n .   strict, rigorous
17. Sc . . . . l . . s   careful, conscientious
18. St . . n . . .   motionless, dull
19. S . r . o . . . l   relating to the art of tailoring
20. S . u . . n . . u .   amazing, astounding
21. S . . p . . . t .   to demand or insist upon as a condition
22. S . . v . . . r .   a docker
23. S . . . t . .   a ghost
24. S . . c . . y   to name or mention expressly

Answers on page 124

Complete the Word — T

Complete the following words from the given meanings.

1. T . m . . s . . . . s   stormy, violent
2. T . . n . . . n .   impermanent, momentary
3. T . . b . . . n .   disturbed, tumultuous
4. To . . r . . .   to endure or permit
5. T . r . . . l   agitation, trouble
6. T . . s . s   a dissertation, exercise
7. T . . . . . t   a three-pronged weapon
8. T . . n . . . t   part of a church
9. T . n . . . . z .   to torment or tease
10. T . . g . . d . . e   a cave-dweller
11. T . . t . t . . .   experimental
12. T . . . . m   a self-evident truth
13. T . . . d . . . y   the art of stuffing and mounting animal skins
14. T . . . s . . a .   a bride's outfit
15. T . . v . . t .   a ridiculous imitation
16. T . a . . u . .   calm, serene
17. T . . p . . l . .   a type of waterproof cloth
18. T . n . . r . . l   relating to a barber
19. T . r . . e   a long speech of denunciation
20. T . a . . c . . . y   the path of a projectile through the air
21. T . . . f . .   frugal, economical
22. T . r . . t . . .   a tract of land, a region
23. T . . . d   lukewarm
24. T . n . . i . . s   holding fast, resolute

Answers on page 124

Complete the Word — U, V, W

Complete the following words from the given meanings.

1. V . v . c . . . s   lively, animated
2. U . d . . . t . . n   rising and falling like waves
3. U . . l . . .   usefulness
4. Va . . . i . .   a holiday
5. V . . t . g .   giddiness, dizziness
6. V . l . . .   courage, prowess
7. V . . n . . . . l .   susceptible of injury, open to attack
8. V . n . . i . .   to conquer or overcome
9. U . b . . .   courteous, suave, refined
10. V . r . i . i . .   a colour
11. W . . m . . .   a soft cry or whine
12. Va . a . . n .   a wanderer or vagrant
13. V . . . f . r . . s   noisy, clamorous
14. U . . n . . . . s   all of one mind, agreeing
15. V . n . . . t .   to regard with respect, revere
16. W . . t . .   to twist or squirm
17. Vi . i . . n . .   watchfulness, caution
18. V . . . i . u . .   a hall or lobby
19. V . r . . c . . . r   native, indigenous
20. W . . . e . n . . .   desert, uninhabited area
21. W . . s . . e   charming, engaging
22. V . n . . c . . v .   revengeful
23. Wi . . n . .   shrivelled, dried up
24. V . . u . . . . n   estimation of worth

Complete the Word

S	T	U, V, W
1. Semaphore	1. Tempestuous	1. Vivacious
2. Sluggish	2. Transient	2. Undulation
3. Soporific	3. Turbulent	3. Utility
4. Synopsis	4. Tolerate	4. Vacation
5. Sinuous	5. Turmoil	5. Vertigo
6. Sepulchral	6. Thesis	6. Valour
7. Sycophant	7. Trident	7. Vulnerable
8. Sardonic	8. Transept	8. Vanquish
9. Subvert	9. Tantalize	9. Urbane
10. Serrated	10. Troglodyte	10. Vermilion
11. Segregate	11. Tentative	11. Whimper
12. Strychnine	12. Truism	12. Vagabond
13. Stamina	13. Taxidermy	13. Vociferous
14. Sacrosanct	14. Trousseau	14. Unanimous
15. Solecism	15. Travesty	15. Venerate
16. Stringent	16. Tranquil	16. Writhe
17. Scrupulous	17. Tarpaulin	17. Vigilance
18. Stagnant	18. Tonsorial	18. Vestibule
19. Sartorial	19. Tirade	19. Vernacular
20. Stupendous	20. Trajectory	20. Wilderness
21. Stipulate	21. Thrifty	21. Winsome
22. Stevedore	22. Territory	22. Vindictive
23. Spectre	23. Tepid	23. Wizened
24. Specify	24. Tenacious	24. Valuation

Four-Letter Words, Latin Words and Last Words

In column 1 are some four-letter words (polite ones!), in column 2 some common Latin phrases, and in column 3 the last common word under each letter. Give their meanings.

1. Adit	1. Bona fide	1. Azure
2. Agog	2. Ad lib	2. Byzantine
3. Avid	3. Sine qua non	3. Czech
4. Awry	4. Ad infinitum	4. Dyspeptic
5. Bode	5. Terra firma	5. Eyrie
6. Cede	6. Status quo	6. Fuzzy
7. Coma	7. Pro tem	7. Gyve
8. Crux	8. Non sequitur	8. Hysterical
9. Dank	9. Tempus fugit	9. Ivy
10. Deft	10. Pro rata	10. Juxtaposition
11. Gist	11. Quid pro quo	11. Kyle
12. Glib	12. In toto	12. Lyrist
13. Hint	13. Ultimo	13. Myxomatosis
14. Icon	14. Per annum	14. Nymphomania
15. Ilex	15. A fortiori	15. Ozonoscope
16. Iota	16. Caveat emptor	16. Pyx
17. Jamb	17. Infra dig	17. Quotient
18. Kink	18. Ipso facto	18. Rye
19. Lyre	19. Ultra vires	19. Systemless
20. Mien	20. Vice versa	20. Tzar
21. Mire	21. Sub judice	21. Vulturous
22. Oast	22. In camera	22. Wyvern
23. Rife	23. Per se	23. Xylophone
24. Tome	24. Ex officio	24. Yule

Four-Letter Words

1. an access or entrance, especially to a mine
2. eager, expectant, on the move
3. greedy, eager
4. uneven, crooked, askew
5. to portend, promise well or ill
6. to give up, grant, surrender
7. state of unnatural, heavy sleep
8. a difficult matter or puzzle
9. wet, exceedingly damp
10. skilful, dextrous, neat
11. the substance of a matter, the essence
12. ready, fluent, easy
13. an indication, suggestion
14. an image or statue
15. species of tree including the holly
16. the Greek Letter I, also a small particle or atom
17. side post of a doorway, window etc., or projecting part of a wall
18. a twist in a rope or wire, a mental twist
19. a stringed musical instrument
20. a person's manner or bearing
21. swamp, bog, mud, dirt
22. hop-drying kiln
23. common, numerous, widespread
24. a large, heavy book

Latin Words

1. in good faith, genuine
2. abbrev. of *ad libitum* – at one's pleasure, as much as one likes
3. indispensable, absolutely necessary
4. without end, for ever
5. dry or firm land, as distinct from the sea or air
6. the existing state of things
7. abbrev. of *pro tempore* – for the time being, temporarily
8. ('it does not follow') – a conclusion which does not follow from the premisses
9. time flies
10. proportionally, in proportion to the value of
11. one thing in place of or in return for another, tit for tat
12. as a whole, completely
13. of last month
14. by the year, yearly
15. with stronger reason
16. let the buyer beware
17. beneath one's dignity
18. by that very fact, by the fact itself
19. beyond the powers or legal authority of
20. in reverse, conversely
21. under consideration of a court or judge
22. in secret, in a closed court
23. by or in itself, intrinsically
24. in discharge of duty, in virtue of one's office

Last Words

1. blue pigment or dye, the colour of the sky
2. relating to Byzantium or its architecture
3. a Bohemian, a native of Czechoslovakia
4. suffering from dyspepsia or indigestion
5. the nest of a bird of prey, especially an eagle
6. not firm or sound, spongy, blurred, fluffy
7. shackle or fetter
8. affected by hysteria, morbidly excited
9. a climbing evergreen shrub
10. the placing of two or more things close together
11. a strait or narrow channel between two islands
12. a player on the lyre, a lyric poet
13. a disease of rabbits
14. morbid sexual desire in females
15. an instrument for measuring the ozone in the air
16. the vessel in which consecrated bread is kept
17. the result obtained by dividing one number by another
18. a species of cereal plant
19. without system
20. the emperor of Russia
21. resembling a vulture, ravenous
22. a legendary animal in the form of a winged dragon
23. a musical instrument
24. Christmas and its festivities